Number

D0489078

ES

impact

MATHS HOMEWORK

Published by Scholastic Ltd,
Villiers House,
Clarendon Avenue,
Leamington Spa,
Warwickshire CV32 5PR

© **1993 Scholastic Ltd**
4 5 6 7 8 9   8 9 0 1 2

 Activities by the IMPACT Project at
the University of North London,
UNIVERSITY OF
NORTH LONDON collated and rewritten by Ruth
Merttens and Ros Leather

Editor Noel Pritchard
Assistant editor Joanne Boden
Designer Anna Oliwa
Series designer Anna Oliwa
Illustrations Mike Gordon
Cover illustration Anna Oliwa

Designed using Aldus Pagemaker
Processed by Salvo Print and Design,
Leamington Spa
Artwork by Steve Williams, Leicester

British Library Cataloguing-in-Publication Data
A catalogue record for this book is
available from the British Library.

ISBN 0-590-53144-1

Number

impact
CONTENTS

Number

impact
CONTENTS

impact
INTRODUCTION

This series of IMPACT books is designed to help you run a non-traditional homework scheme. Through the use of take-home maths activities, children can share maths with a parent/carer in the context of the home. The results of these activities then feed back into the classwork at school.

IMPACT works through the following processes:
● Teachers plan their maths for the next few weeks as usual and consider which parts might usefully be done at home.
● Teachers look through selected activities which fit in with what they are planning.
● The activities are photocopied and sent home with the children every week or fortnight.
● The results of each activity are brought back into the classroom by the children and form part of the following week's classwork.

In practice this process will be slightly different in each classroom and in each school. Teachers may adapt it to fit their own way of working and the ethos of the school. Most schools send out IMPACT activities fortnightly, although some do send it weekly. There is some evidence to suggest that weekly activities get a slightly better response and help to raise standards more effectively than fortnightly, but this is not conclusive. The important point is that each teacher should feel comfortable with how often IMPACT is used in his/her class.

Planning

When you, the teacher, are looking at your work and deciding what maths, roughly speaking, you plan to be doing over the next few weeks, all that is necessary is to consider which parts may usefully be done or practised at home. It is helpful if, over a period of time, a variety of activities are chosen. These tend to fall into three broad categories:
● Activities which practise a skill – these are useful in that they can be followed up in the routine classwork the children are doing. They must be carefully selected according to the level of the children.
● Activities which collect data – these lead into work on data-handling and representation.
● Activities in which children measure or make something – this produces an object or some measurements to be used later in class.

The activities in this book are divided into four sections according to age: Year 3, Year 4, Year 5 and Year 6. There are two pages of teachers' notes relating to the individual activities at the beginning of each section. Links to National Curriculum attainment targets are included in the teachers' notes and numerals in brackets refer to the programmes of study, so AT 2/1 (iii, iv) refers to Attainment Target 2, Level 1, Programmes of Study 3 and 4. Details of how these relate to the curricula in Scotland and Northern Ireland are given on page 128.

Working with parents

It is important for the success of IMPACT that the activities taken home are seen by the parents to be maths. We always suggest, at least until IMPACT is up and running and parents' confidence in it is well established, that activities are chosen which have a clearly mathematical purpose. Save the more 'wacky' activities until later! You will get a much better response if parents believe that what they are doing is maths.

Each activity contains a note to parents which explains the purpose of the activity and how they can best help. It also gives a reference to National Curriculum attainment targets – although not to any level. Teachers who prefer not to have these can white them out. The IMPACT activities should be accompanied by an IMPACT diary, enabling parents and children to make their comments. See page 128 for details.

Making the most of IMPACT

The quickest way to reduce the number of children who share the maths at home is to ignore or be negative about what they bring back. When the children come running into the classroom, tripping over the string which went twice round their cat, it is difficult to welcome them all individually but it is crucial that the activities done at home are followed up in classwork. The nature and type of this follow-up work depends very much upon the nature of the activity, and specific suggestions are made in the teachers' notes. However, some general points apply:
● Number activities, such as games, can often be repeated in a more formalised way in the classwork. For example, if the children have been playing a dice game, throwing two dice and adding the totals, they can continue to do this in the classroom, but this time they can record all the 'sums' in their maths book. This applies to any skills-practice activity.
● Data-collecting activities, of any description, need to be followed up by allowing the children to work together in small groups and collate, analyse and represent their joint data. This will inevitably involve children in a discussion as to how their data was obtained, and any problems they had obtaining it.
● If the children have made or measured something at home, the information or the object needs to be used as part of the classwork. This will not be too difficult since this type of activity is selected by the teacher precisely in order to provide the measurements or shapes for use in class.

The implication of this is that it is wise to select a variety of activities to send home. No teacher wants to drown in data, nor do they want all the IMPACT activities to result in more routine number work. Some activities generate lots of follow-up work while others simply require minimal follow-up – perhaps just a discussion about who won and who lost, and how many times people played.

Many of the activities can lead to an attractive display or enable the teacher to make a class book. Such a book does not have to be 'grand'. It can be simply five or six large sheets of sugar paper folded in the middle and stitched/stapled with the children's work mounted inside it. The children love these books, and they make a fine record of their work. An IMPACT display board in the school entrance hall gives parents a sense that their work at home is appreciated.

For further details of IMPACT see page 128.

Teachers' Notes
YEAR THREE

The activities in this book also address aspects of the Programme of Study for Number. In particular, this section utilises the following skills:

● reading, writing and ordering the whole the numbers up to 999, and occasionally beyond;

● understanding place value;

● performing addition, subtraction, multiplication and division (as sharing) calculations in practical and real-life contexts;

● estimating and approximating numbers up to 999;

● using a variety of methods of computations according to the context of the problem;

● investigating the different outcomes of simple open-ended mathematical puzzles and tricks, and

● using fractions, particularly in practical and real-life contexts;

● working with and developing number patterns, including sequences, even and odds, addition and multiplication-table patterns.

Smarty pants Use coloured cubes to represent Smarties. Compare the children's results and make a line of colours from most likely to occur to least likely. Discuss the position of the different colours along the line.

Holiday week Make a large floor map of your local area. Ask children to devise a game involving visiting places in the neighbourhood. They could discuss journeys they make in the neighbourhood.

Road numbers Make an ordered collection of the road numbers and discuss which numbered cards would divide into the road numbers. Which numbers have the most/least number of multiplies? Do all numbers have multiples?

Patchwork quilt Children may like to design their own patchwork quilts working in pairs. These could be joined together to create a class quilt. Number games could be played, for example if a child says half, his partner must say two quarters or half. This will help them to understand how fractions work.

Rat run Children can invent their own rat runs back in the classroom. What happens if they use the operations (x, ÷, −, +) in a different order. Can they use other aspects of numbers, for example whether a number is prime or not? Whether a number is square? Make a series of rat runs for display purposes.

Three score and what? Children can compare the differences between their numbers. Who got the largest? Can they play the same game in class, only this time the aim is to arrange the digits so as to make two different sums and get the smallest difference between the answers.

Coin turn over To extend the concept of probability this activity could be adapted

for three groups of children. Each group chooses a different combination from the three choices: colour and suit; colour and number; suit and number. Children can then compare and investigte the results.

Leaping dolphins Extend the activity by using 13 dolphins or ask the children to make up some new rules for the game. The children can work in groups to try a similar activity sing three pools.

Age discovery Children can work in groups to try to discover other methods of working out people's age. These could then be displayed and shared. Can the children think of other numbers they can 'discover' for example each other's house or flat numbers? What about creating a puzzle to discover someone's telephone number? This may need a calculator.

Memory bonds This is a good game for children to play in spare moments. The follow-up for this activity may well be incorporated into children's routine number work. They can formalise the game by writing down the numbers in their maths booksas they play. However, this does slow the game down and so should only be done once.

Memory difference This activity is an extension of 'Memory bonds' and therefore can be followed up in much the same way.

Animal voices Perhaps the children could adapt the game to make it quieter for the classroom! The children can play the same game using cards made in the classroom with larger numbers on. This will increase the difficulty and hopefully not the noise!

Spoon money Ask the children to fit money into a spoon and, once the coins spill out, they must total their spoonful. Who had the most money? Children can work in pairs to make new totals and then arrange themselves in value order.

Target number Children could play this game with a partner to stimulate discussion. Tens and units counting apparatus could be used to represent their answers. Ask the children to write down the answers to calculations such as: Take away 20. tale awa 10. These could be checked with the counting apparatus.

Digital debate Make a digital and an analogue timeline with pictures to show significant events during the day. Children could stick their digital times on to the timeline.

Hung, drawn and quartered Children could work in pairs beginning with, say four, and find out whch numbers could be quartered. These could be recorded on a number line in a different colour.

Dart decisions Children could exchange dartboards. Using a number line they could check how many numbers up to 100 they have found. What is the least number of segments required to find all the numbers up to 100?

Spend, spend, spend This game could be used with a group of chidren in spare moments and is excellent for encouraging mental arithmetic and calculator skills. Ask the children to estimate the answer before using the calculator. It is important for children to estimate, it will help them to understand whether their answer is sensible.

Zoo numbers Children can invent their own multiplication bingo games in class. What numbers is it sensible to use? Which numbers can they never get if they are multiplying two card numbers. Talk about prime numbers with lots of factors. What happens if they are using dice and not cards? Can they design a game for dice?

Legs count up Children can combine their findings. What displays can you make to go around the three times table? What different numbers of sets of threes? And how about fours? Were there any numbers for which it was hard to find examples? Can they find any examples of these in class? Perhaps they can make a display to go round every number up to six ... or up to ten?

Money times tables Children will be able to write out their tables in class. They will also need to write out some of the tables you cannot make using coins. A display of the various coins can be attractive. This will help to reinforce the notion of value.

Monster multiplying This activity can be followed up with work on different 'types' of monster to practise different tables! This can be done in groups and can lead to some wonderful art work and displays.

When the children have worked on a partiular monster, they can learn the times tables - at least up to six times.

Multiplication rhymes This activity really leads into the learning table. The children can be encouraged to write out and display their rhymes in the appropriate set (according to which times table it is). Do any tables not have poems? Can they write them in groups - or as a class then say eazch table out loud as a class? Different children can learn a particular table, depending upon their poem.

Cross patches Children can play this game in class. They can invent a more difficult version using larger numbers. What target number will they need to use in this case? Can you make a display of all their different games? Who is the champion?

Rhyming numbers Children can write out and display their lists of rhyming words alongside a large representation of each times table. Use their words to help them learn tables facts. Chanting the tables is is a useful follow-up, as is counting round the class in fours or fives or sixes and so on.

Shapey tables Children will need to talk about the types of shapes they have used. What are their names? For example any six-sided shape is a hexagon. What tables have they generated from their shapes? Can they recite the tables out loud in class, and try other strategies? They can design tables tests for each other, in which they draw up a list of questions and a specially-shaped box for the answer according to which table it is in!

Six digit trick Children will need to talk about their big numbers. Can they classify them in sets, for example all the numbers between 850,000 and 950,000 in one set. and so pon. This will really help children to consider what each digit in a large numner actually stands for. Working in a group, they can also order their big numbers from largest to smallest.

Times table endings When the children bring their work back into class, look first at all the household or personal things they have attached to each table. Perhaps a brief display of all the things they have found around the chosen table will help to focus their attention. Go on to recite the tables and also make sure they have built each table up using sets of objects, for example Multilink towers.

Vehicle tables practice Children's drawings could be used to make a really nice display. Arrange them around a large version of the relevant table. When you rehearse these tables in class, children can always 'cheat' by peeking at the display!

Eggscentric arrangements This investigation can be followed up in class by asking the children to prove to you that they have found all the possible arrangements for each number of eggs. How do they structure and order their search, and their findings? Make a display of the best ways.

Tens and units designer label These labels can be used to make a nice display. Some children may want to do another in class. A nice extension is to try to make a label where there is a 'hundreds' digit. You will need very small squares on the paper!

Jumping fractions In class, it is important to talk about the remainders. Which numbers can be divided into halves? What do we call these numbers? How do we find one half? What is one half of a half? The children can find quarters and eighths in class and then formalise this work in their maths books - without the jumping!

_____and

child

_____

helper(s)

_____

did this activity together

Smarty pants

YOU WILL NEED: a small box of Smarties.

● Count the number of Smarties and write the answer in the circle.

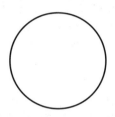

● Count how many there are of each colour and write the numbers in the circles below.

● Put the Smarties into a bag or back into the box and shake them up.

● Shut your eyes and take 1 out. Before you look at it, guess what colour it will be.

● Score 1 point if you are right. Do not put it back!

● Do this 10 times. How many points have you scored?

Can you improve on this score?

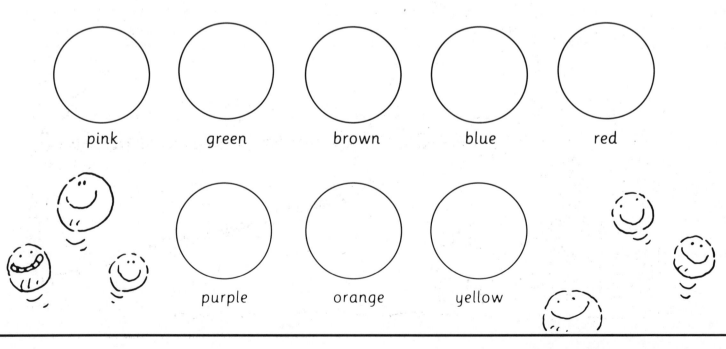

pink   green   brown   blue   red

purple   orange   yellow

Holiday week

YOU WILL NEED: a dice and 7 counters for each player.

● You must begin and end your journey in Oxford.

● Take it in turns to throw the dice.

● Move the number of stations indicated by the number thrown.

● You must visit (land on) 7 different places, leaving a counter at each destination.

● The first player to do this is the winner!

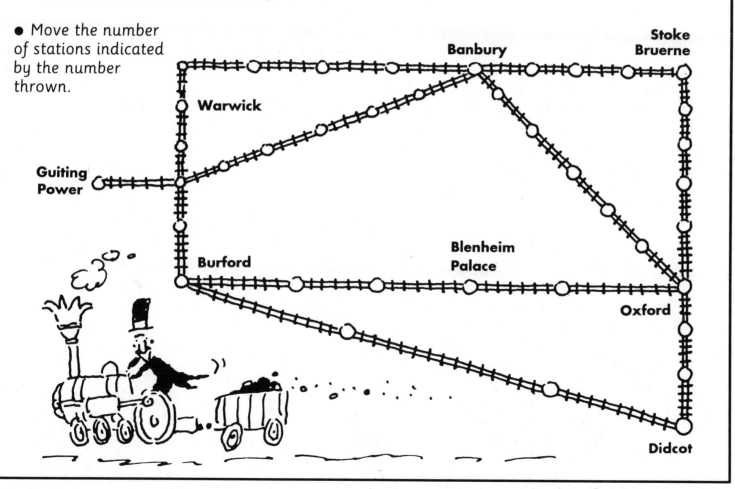

Dear Parent or Carer

You will need some way of marking the stations that you have visited. Can you develop any strategies which will help you to complete the game? Are these strategies fair?

_____and

child

_____

helper(s)

_____

did this activity together

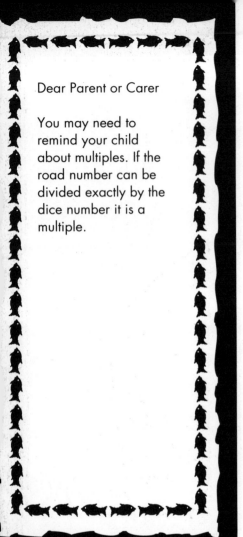

_____and

child

_____

helper(s)

_____

did this activity together

Road numbers

YOU WILL NEED: a counter for each player; the board (on the accompanying sheet) and cards labelled 2, 3, 4, 5, 6, 7, 8 and 9. (You can make these by cutting up the backs of old Christmas or birthday cards, or you could use just those numbers from a pack of playing cards!)

● Place the cards in a pile, face down.

● Place all the counters on 'Start'.

● Take it in turns to turn over the top card.

● Move your counter along a connecting road BUT the road number must be a multiple of the number on the card and there can be only 1 counter on a junction at any one time.

● You are not allowed to move if the road number is not a multiple of the card or if the next junction is covered! You are in a traffic jam, held up on your way to the beach!

● Replace the card on the bottom of the pile and let another player take a turn.

Who reaches the seaside first?

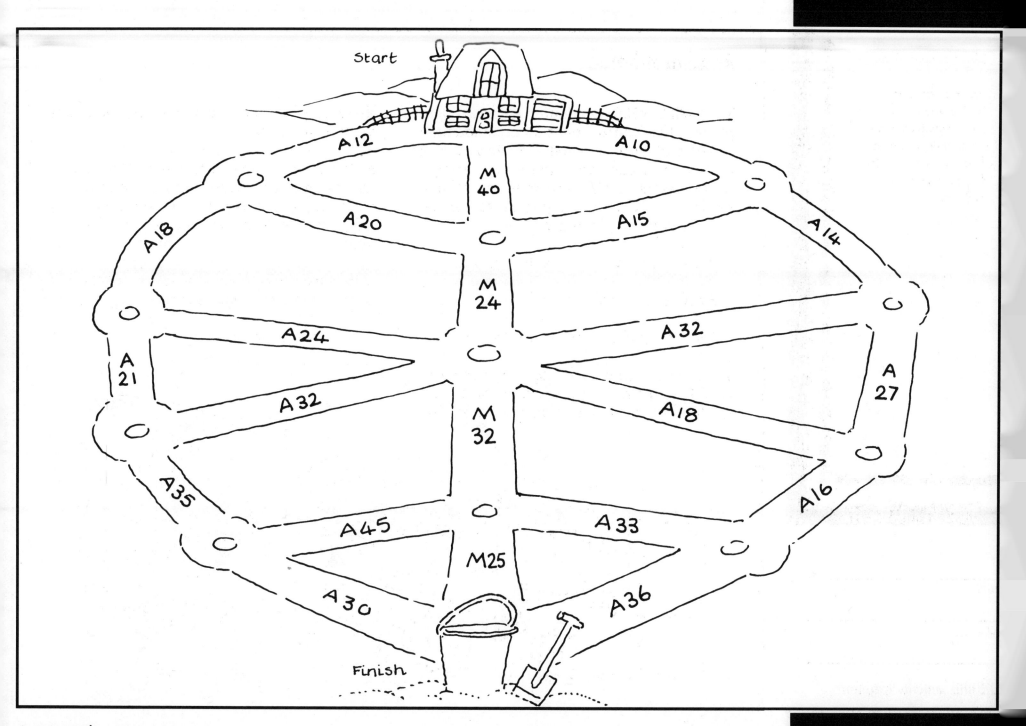

Start

A12   A10

M
40

A18   A20   A15   A14

M
24

A24   A32

A
21   A
27

A32   A18

M
32

A35   A45   A33   A16

M25

A30   A36

Finish

Patchwork quilt

YOU WILL NEED: a pair of scissors; 2 different coloured pencils for each player and the patchwork quilt on the accompanying sheet.

● Cut out all the fraction cards at the bottom of the page. (The cards will last longer if you stick them on to an old birthday or Christmas card.)

● Shuffle them and place them in a pile, face down.

● Choose 2 different coloured crayons each.

●. Turn over the top card and look at the patchwork quilt. Shade in a square divided into that fraction (such as halves) in your colours.

● Replace the card on the bottom of the pile and let someone else take a turn.

● Can you complete the patchwork?

half	whole	one quarter	two quarters	three quarters	whole
$\dfrac{1}{2}$	$\dfrac{2}{2}$	$\dfrac{1}{4}$	$\dfrac{2}{4}$	$\dfrac{3}{4}$	$\dfrac{4}{4}$

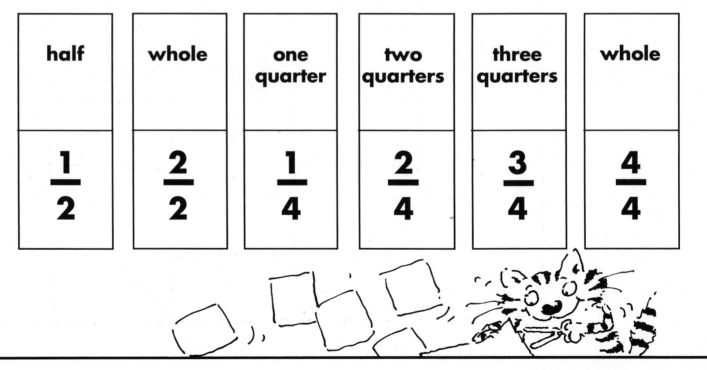

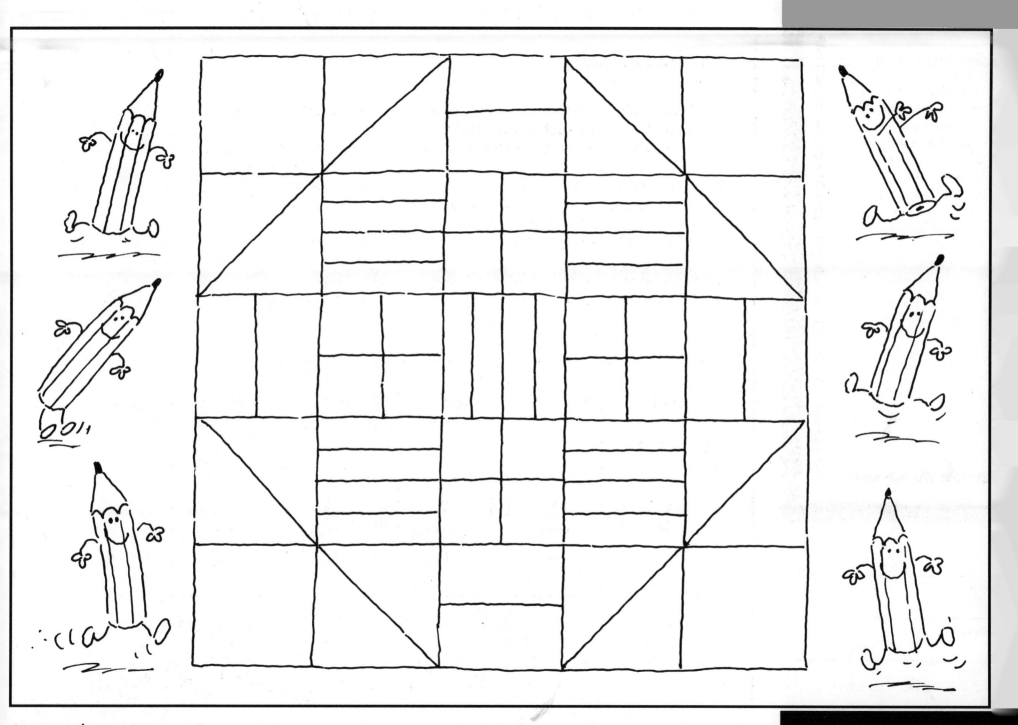

_____and

child

_____

helper(s)

_____

did this activity together

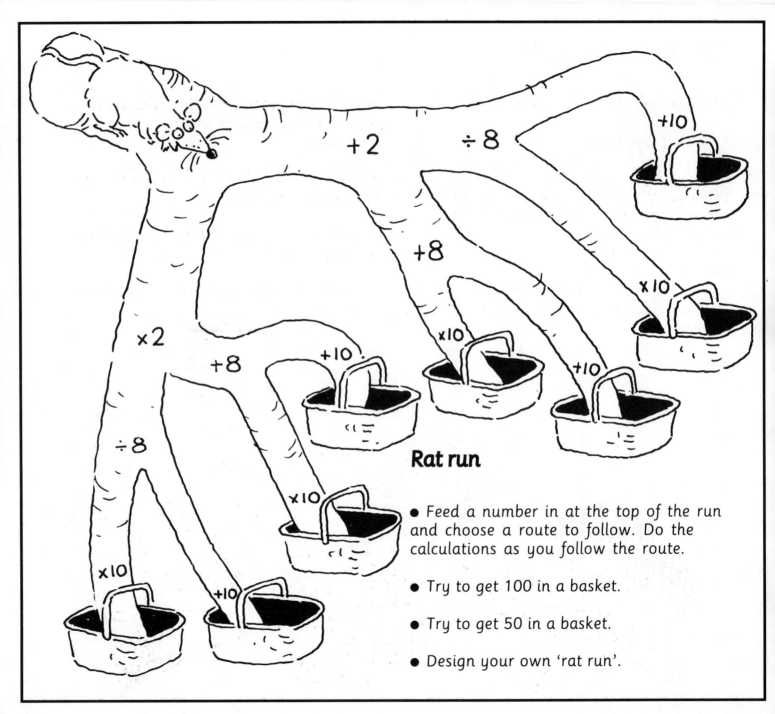

Rat run

- Feed a number in at the top of the run and choose a route to follow. Do the calculations as you follow the route.

- Try to get 100 in a basket.

- Try to get 50 in a basket.

- Design your own 'rat run'.

impact MATHS HOMEWORK

Three score and what?

YOU WILL NEED: a dice and a pencil.

● Roll the dice twice.

● Make a 2-figure number from the numbers thrown. Now reverse the two numbers to make another number. Which number is highest?

● Roll the dice twice again to make another number and reverse the digits again so that you have 2 numbers. Which number is highest?

● Add together the 2 highest numbers from each set. Now add together the two lowest numbers.

● What is the difference between the two totals? This is your score.

● Take 3 turns each. What is the highest score you can get?

● The player with the highest score is the winner.

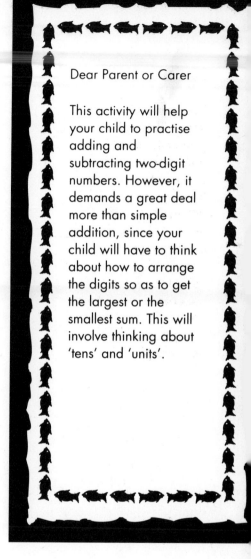

Dear Parent or Carer

This activity will help your child to practise adding and subtracting two-digit numbers. However, it demands a great deal more than simple addition, since your child will have to think about how to arrange the digits so as to get the largest or the smallest sum. This will involve thinking about 'tens' and 'units'.

_____and

child

_____

helper(s)

_____

did this activity together

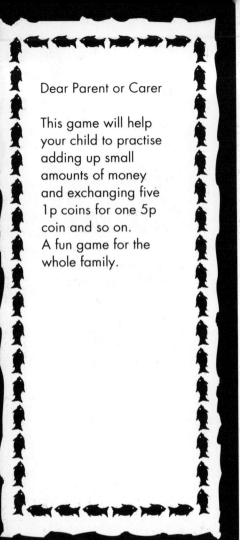
Coin turn over

YOU WILL NEED: a pile of small bricks – such as Lego; a handful of coins and a pack of cards.

● Place the cards, face down, in the middle of the table. Put the handful of coins beside them.

● Turn over the top card but, before you turn it over, try to predict 3 things about it. For example: number, suit and colour.

● Take it in turns to play and take 1 penny for each correct prediction.

● As you collect larger amounts you may exchange your coins for others on the pile.

● The winner is whoever ends up with the most money.

impact MATHS HOMEWORK

Leaping dolphins

YOU WILL NEED: coloured crayons; a large version of the board opposite; the 7 dolphin counters from the bottom of the page and a dice.

● Colour the 7 dolphin counters in different colours and cut them out.

● Place the dolphins in the pools in any order you like.

● Throw the dice and move that number of dolphins from one pool to another. No dolphin can move twice (into a new pool and back again!) in any 1 turn.

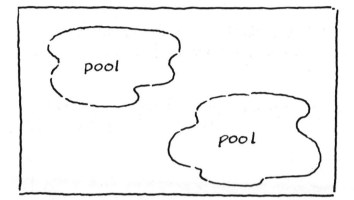

● Continue to play. Can you get all the dolphins in the same pool?

● Can you get 6 dolphins in 1 pool and 1 in another?

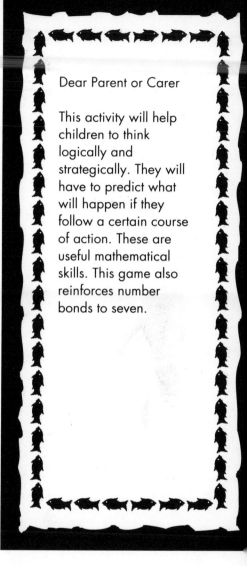

Dear Parent or Carer

This activity will help children to think logically and strategically. They will have to predict what will happen if they follow a certain course of action. These are useful mathematical skills. This game also reinforces number bonds to seven.

_____and
child

_____
helper(s)

_____
did this activity together

_____and

child

_____

helper(s)

_____

did this activity together

Age discovery

Find out how old people are without them telling you! Try it out on your family first then surprise your friends!

Here's how to do it.

Suppose Sam is 8. Tell him he must follow your instructions exactly.

> **Take his age - he must not tell you!**
> **Multiply it by 5   = 40**
> **Add 20   = 60**
> **Double it   = 120**
> **Subtract 30   = 90**
> **Divide it by 10   = 9**
> **Tell you his answer, in this case 9**
>
> **You quietly take away 1.**
> **This is his age!**

Can you figure out why this works?

impact MATHS HOMEWORK

Memory bonds

YOU WILL NEED: a pack of playing cards from which the face cards and the 10s have been removed.

● Deal out the cards in 4 rows of 9, face down.

● Turn over any 2 cards.

● If they add up to 10, take them both and keep them. If not, turn them back over.

● Take it in turns to play until all the cards are gone or you cannot continue.

● Count up your pairs. The player with the most pairs is the winner.

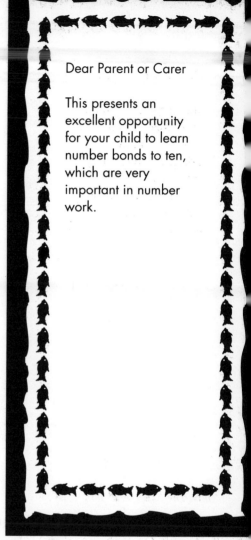

_____and

child

_____

helper(s)

_____

did this activity together

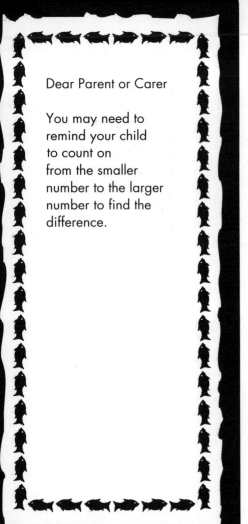
Memory difference

YOU WILL NEED: a pack of playing cards with the face cards removed.

● Arrange your cards in 4 rows of 10, face down.

● Turn over any 2 cards.

● Work out the difference between them. For example:

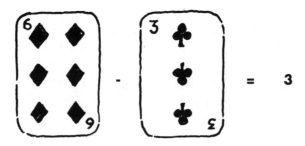

● If they have a difference of 2, you may keep the pair.

● If not, turn them back over.

● Take it in turns to play until there are no pairs left with a difference of 2.

● Count up your pairs. The player with the most is the winner.

impact MATHS HOMEWORK

Animal voices

YOU WILL NEED: 2 dice; an empty egg box and some coloured counters.

Each player must choose an animal to imitate!

● Share out the counters (one colour for each player) and each choose a section of the egg box to use.

● Take it in turns to throw 2 dice.

● If the numbers thrown add up to 4, 5, or 6 the player throwing the dice must make that number of animal noises. (Such as bark 4 times!)

● If the numbers thrown add up to 8, 9, or 10 everyone, except the player throwing the dice, must make that number of animal noises!

● If the numbers thrown add up to 2, 3, 11, or 12, the player throwing the dice must write down that number and put a counter of their colour in their section of the egg box.

● Take it in turns to play. The first player to reach a score of 30 by multiplying the number of counters in their section of the egg box by the highest number they have written down is the winner!

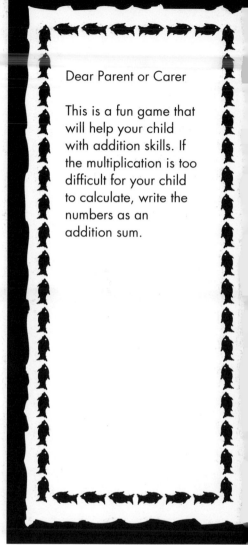

Dear Parent or Carer

This is a fun game that will help your child with addition skills. If the multiplication is too difficult for your child to calculate, write the numbers as an addition sum.

_____and

child

_____

helper(s)

_____

did this activity together

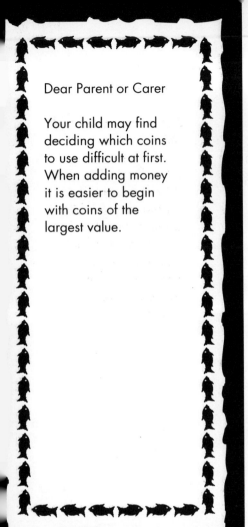

_____and

child

_____

helper(s)

_____

did this activity together

Spoon money

YOU WILL NEED: a handful of coins; a dice and a dessertspoon for each player.

● Take it in turns to throw the dice and take the amount of money, indicated by the number thrown, from the pile of coins. So a 5 could be:

or

● Put the coins in the spoon. (Your aim is to fit as much money as possible into the spoon!)

● If the coins spill out you have to empty your spoon and start again!

● Take 10 turns each. The player with the most money in their spoon at the end is the winner.

impact MATHS HOMEWORK

Target number

YOU WILL NEED: a pencil; a pack of cards with the face cards removed and a blank score sheet like the one shown for each player.

● Place the cards, face down, in a pile.

● Pick up a card and decide where to place it on your board (either in the tens or units column). Once you have put it down, you may not move it! Now write down your score.

● Take 5 turns each, adding up the numbers and writing down your score each time.

The winner is the player who makes a number closest to 55!

● Play several times. Do you get better?

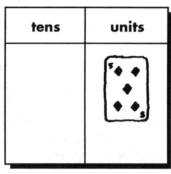

tens	units

score = 5

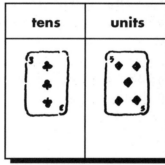

tens	units

score = 35

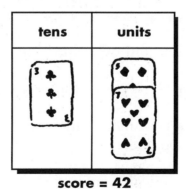

tens	units

score = 42

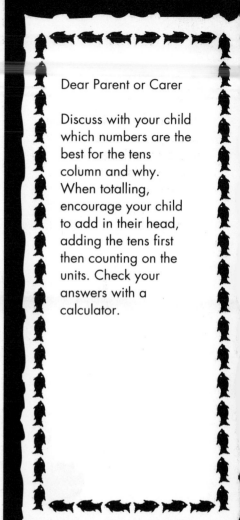
_____and

child

_____

helper(s)

_____

did this activity together

_____and

child

_____

helper(s)

_____

did this activity together

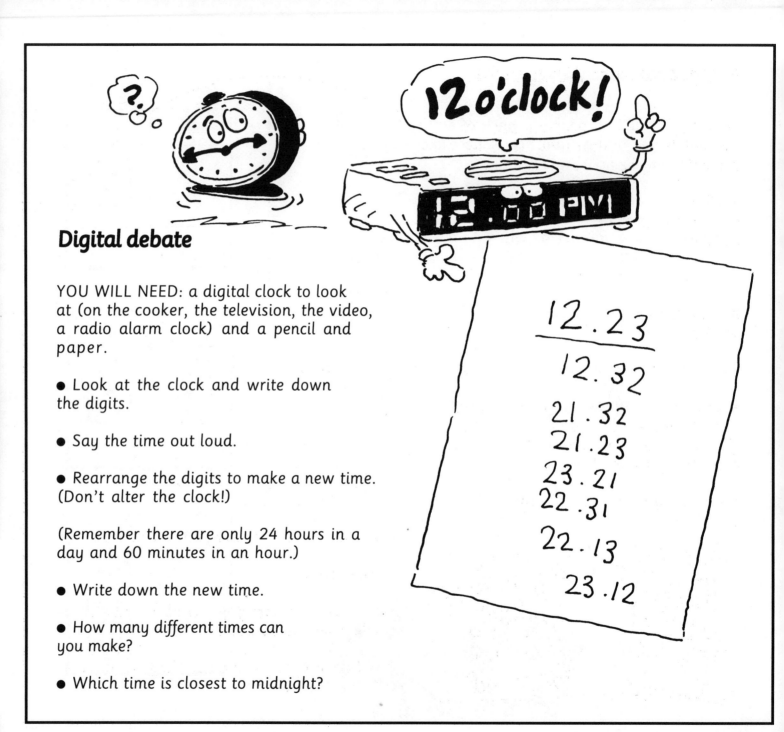

Digital debate

YOU WILL NEED: a digital clock to look at (on the cooker, the television, the video, a radio alarm clock) and a pencil and paper.

● Look at the clock and write down the digits.

● Say the time out loud.

● Rearrange the digits to make a new time. (Don't alter the clock!)

(Remember there are only 24 hours in a day and 60 minutes in an hour.)

● Write down the new time.

● How many different times can you make?

● Which time is closest to midnight?

12.23
12.32
21.32
21.23
23.21
22.31
22.13
23.12

impact MATHS HOMEWORK

Hung, drawn and quartered

YOU WILL NEED: a dice; counters, such as small bricks, buttons, or dried pasta; a pencil and paper and a calculator!

● Throw the dice twice. Write down both numbers to make a 2-figure number.

So: **1 and 6 = 16**

● Reverse them to make a second number:

61

● You are looking for numbers which can be divided into 4 quarters exactly. If it helps, you can share out the counters on to the circle to check.

● Decide which number (if any) is best.

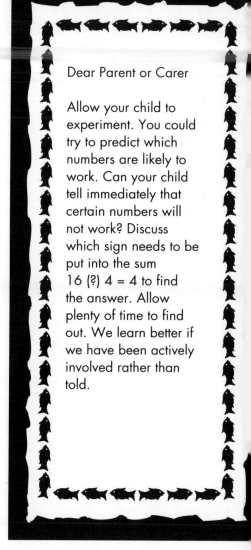

Dear Parent or Carer

Allow your child to experiment. You could try to predict which numbers are likely to work. Can your child tell immediately that certain numbers will not work? Discuss which sign needs to be put into the sum 16 (?) 4 = 4 to find the answer. Allow plenty of time to find out. We learn better if we have been actively involved rather than told.

● Check your sum using the calculator:

16 ÷ 4 = 4

● Score 10 points if you choose a number which can be quartered.

● Take it in turns to play. The first to reach 100 is the winner!

_____and
child

_____
helper(s)

_____

did this activity together

_____and

child

_____

helper(s)

_____

did this activity together

Dart decisions

This is the dartboard. You may throw 3 darts.

- What is the highest possible score?

- What is the lowest?

- How many different scores can you make?

- Design your own dartboard so that you could score every number less than 100 in 3 darts.

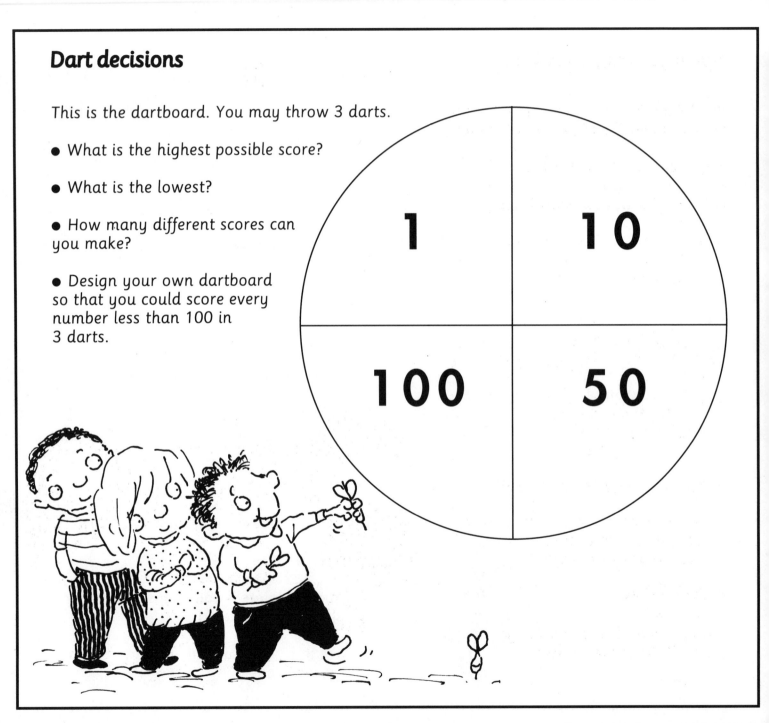

impact MATHS HOMEWORK

Spend, spend, spend

YOU WILL NEED: a calculator for each player; a pencil and paper and a dice.

Everybody starts with £100!

● Enter 100 on your calculator.

● Take it in turns to throw the dice 3 times. This is the amount you have to spend. For example:

£4.36

● Subtract this from your £100.

● Suggest something that you could actually buy with that amount and write it down. Such as:

£4.36 paints

● Keep playing. The first player to get below £5.00 is the winner.

Dear Parent or Carer

Your child will be required to make many subtractions when you play this game. Can your child estimate the new total each time before using the calculator? You could extend this game by asking whether there is another way of arranging the dice to reduce the amount more quickly.

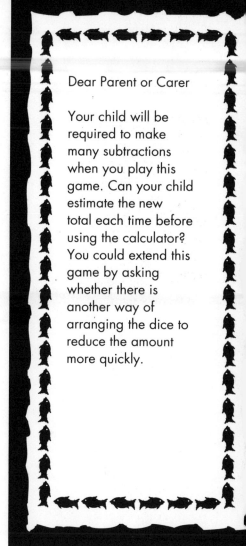

_____and

child

_____

helper(s)

_____

did this activity together

Zoo numbers

YOU WILL NEED: a pack of cards with the face cards removed; counters or dried pasta and a calculator to sort out arguments!

● Place the cards in a pile, face down, in the middle of the table.

● Pick up 2 cards.

● Multiply the 2 cards together. Say the answer out loud. (If you are not sure whether you are right, check it on the calculator.)

● If this is the same as a number on one of the animals, put a counter on that animal.

● If there is already a counter on an animal, you must choose an animal and imitate the noise it makes!

● Replace the cards on the bottom of the pile.

● Take it in turns to play.

● The player to cover the last animal is the winner!

impact MATHS HOMEWORK

Legs count up

● Look around your house for a piece of furniture, an animal, or anything else, which has legs!

● Draw it in the space on the right.

● Now work out:

How many legs would 2 of these have?

How many legs would 3 of these have?

How many legs would 4 of these have?

How many legs would 5 of these have?

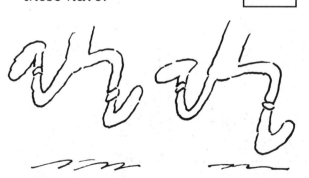

Dear Parent or Carer

This activity will help your child to develop a clear idea of what multiplication involves - i.e. that 3 x 4 means three sets of four. We shall be building on this work as we come to learn our tables.

_____and

child

_____

helper(s)

_____

did this activity together

_____and

child

_____

helper(s)

_____

did this activity together

Money times tables

We can use money to help us learn our
tables! For example:

1 x 5 = 5p

2 x 5 = 5p + 5p = 10p

3 x 5 = 5p + 5p + 5p = 15p

● Continue this table up to 10 x 5p.

● Now can you write another times table
using a 2p or a 10p coin?

● If you feel really brave you could try
working out the first few lines of the table
for 20p!

impact MATHS HOMEWORK

Monster multiplying

Here is a monster. It has 3 arms,
3 fingers on each hand and 3 eyes!

- How many fingers does it have?

- How many arms do 2 monsters have?

- Fill in the chart below.

	arms	fingers
1 monster		
2 monsters		
3 monsters		
4 monsters		
5 monsters		
6 monsters		
7 monsters		
8 monsters		
9 monsters		
10 monsters		

Dear Parent or Carer

This activity will help your child to understand the concept of multiplication.
As well as knowing the answer to the question, 'What are three fours?', it is important – especially for later work in multiplication and division – that children understand what we mean by multiplication.

_____and

child

_____

helper(s)

_____

did this activity together

Multiplication rhymes

Make up a rhyme with a multiplication table in it!

For example:

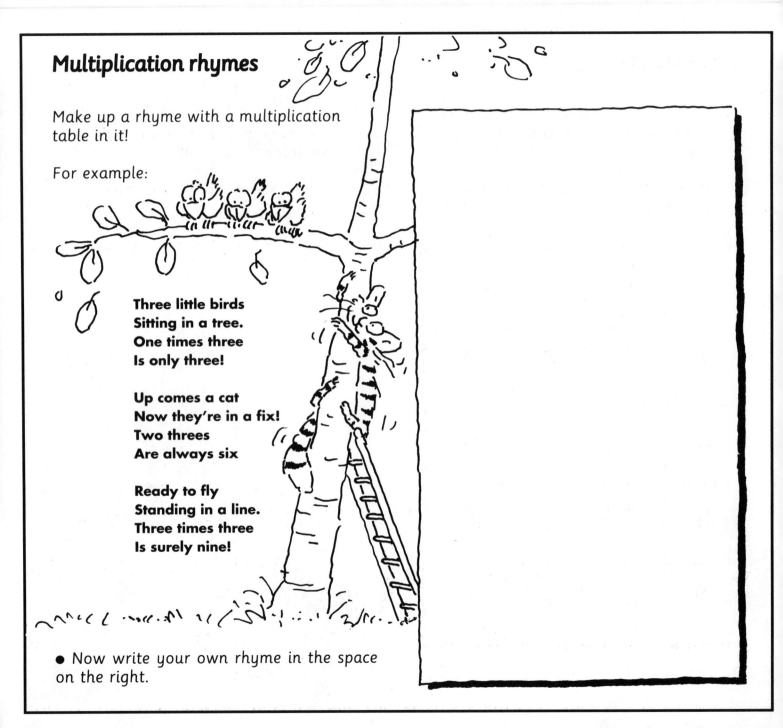

**Three little birds
Sitting in a tree.
One times three
Is only three!**

**Up comes a cat
Now they're in a fix!
Two threes
Are always six**

**Ready to fly
Standing in a line.
Three times three
Is surely nine!**

● Now write your own rhyme in the space on the right.

Cross patches

YOU WILL NEED: a piece of paper (you could use the back of this one) and a pencil for each player.

● Take it in turns to cross out numbers from the grid.

5	4	3	2
1	5	4	3
2	1	5	4
3	2	1	5
4	3	2	1

● As you cross out the numbers you must add them together, keeping a total of only those you have crossed out.

● The first player to cross out numbers which add up to 29 exactly is the winner.

● Play 3 games. Take it in turns to go first. Do you have a winning strategy?

Dear Parent or Carer

This activity involves much more strategic thinking than you may first assume! Your child (and you!) will do a great deal of mental arithmetic but you will also need to develop a winning strategy!

_____and

child

_____

helper(s)

_____

did this activity together

_____and

child

_____

helper(s)

_____

did this activity together

Rhyming numbers

● Write out a times table using any number above 2.

● Write it out like this:

1 x 5 = 5

2 x 5 = 10

3 x 5 = 15

4 x 5 = 20

… all the way up to 10 times.

● Say the table out loud at least 6 times.

● Now can you write a list of words which rhyme with the numbers at the end of each line? Such as:

5 alive

10 hen

15 bean

20 plenty

… and so on.

Shapey tables

● Choose a shape and draw it. It must have straight sides. See the example in diagram A.

● How many sides does it have?

● Now draw 2 of your shapes. They must touch at one corner. See diagram B.

● How many sides are there now?

● Now draw 3 of your shapes. They must each touch another shape at one corner. See diagram C.

● How many sides are there now?

● Continue drawing shapes and counting sides until you have drawn 5 touching shapes.

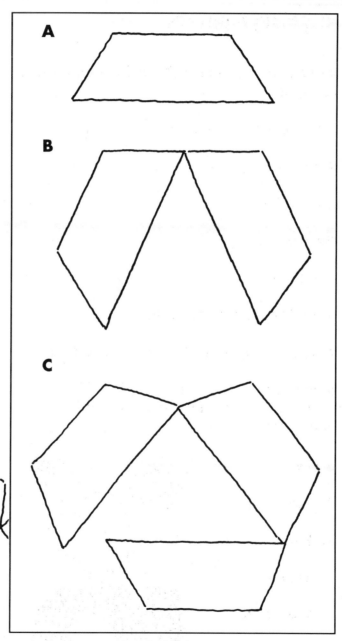

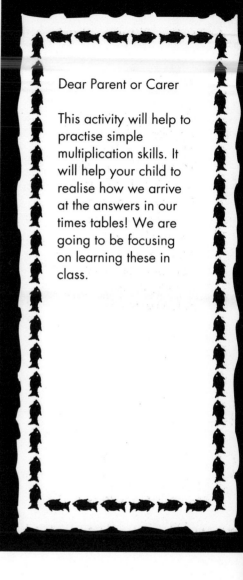
_____and

child

_____

helper(s)

_____

did this activity together

_____and

child

_____

helper(s)

_____

did this activity together

Six digit trick

Ask someone to choose a 3-digit number.

● Write it down. For example:

793

● Repeat the 3 digits to create a 6-digit number.

793793

● Tell them you know what the answer will be when you divide their 6-digit number by 7, then by 11 and by 13! For example:

793793 ÷ 7 = 113399

113399 ÷ 11 = 10309

10309 ÷ 13 = 793 (The original number!)

● Write the answer secretly on a piece of paper and then do the divisions. Use a calculator to help you.

● Try other 3-digit numbers
Does this trick always work?

impact MATHS HOMEWORK

onetwo is two..
two two's are four...
three...

Times tables endings

- Can you fill in the blanks below?

- Numbers in the 2 times table end in:

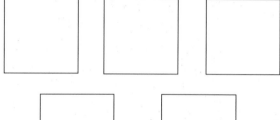

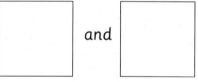 and

- Numbers in the 5 times table end in:

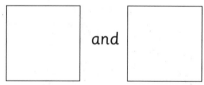 and

- Numbers in the 10 times table end in:

- Make a list of the numbers which are in all 3 tables.

- Find something at home or within your family to go with each one! Such as:

Your dad has 10 goldfish!

Dear Parent or Carer

This activity will focus your child's attention on times tables. We are looking for ways to help remember them. Please help!

_____and

child

_____

helper(s)

_____

did this activity together

_____and

child

_____

helper(s)

_____

did this activity together

Vehicle tables practice

● Complete these 3 tables.

1 x 2 = 2	1 x 3 = 3	1 x 4 = 4
2 x 2 =	2 x 3 =	2 x 4 =
3 x 2 = 6	3 x 3 =	3 x 4 =
4 x 2 =	4 x 3 = 12	4 x 4 = 16
5 x 2 =	5 x 3 =	5 x 4 =
6 x 2 = 12	6 x 3 =	6 x 4 = 24
7 x 2 =	7 x 3 = 21	7 x 4 =
8 x 2 = 16	8 x 3 =	8 x 4 =
9 x 2 =	9 x 3 =	9 x 4 = 36
10 x 2 =	10 x 3 = 30	10 x 4 =

● Find someone to listen then say the 2 times table twice out loud, the 3 times table 3 times and the 4 times table 4 times.

● Now draw:
a vehicle with 2 wheels
a vehicle with 3 wheels
a vehicle with 4 wheels.

impact MATHS HOMEWORK

Eggscentric arrangements

YOU WILL NEED: an egg box and small objects, such as raisins, toy bricks or buttons.

● How many ways can you place 1 egg in an egg box? Use small objects, such as raisins, to try out the different arrangements.

● Now try using 2 eggs. How many different arrangements can you find?

● How about 3 eggs?

● Can you predict how many for 4 eggs?

● What if you use a 12 egg box?

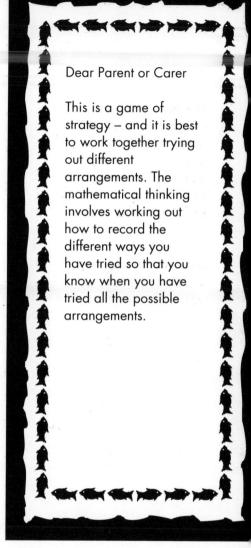

Dear Parent or Carer

This is a game of strategy – and it is best to work together trying out different arrangements. The mathematical thinking involves working out how to record the different ways you have tried so that you know when you have tried all the possible arrangements.

_____and

child

_____

helper(s)

_____

did this activity together

_____and

child

_____

helper(s)

_____

did this activity together

Tens and units designer label

YOU WILL NEED: squared paper; felt-tipped pens and a creative mind!

● Draw a number between 11 and 100 on the squared paper.

> BUT the number must be drawn so that the units figure covers that number of squares. For example: **26** (6 covers 6 squares) and the tens figure covers that number of squares (20 covers 20 squares).

● Make your own designer label!

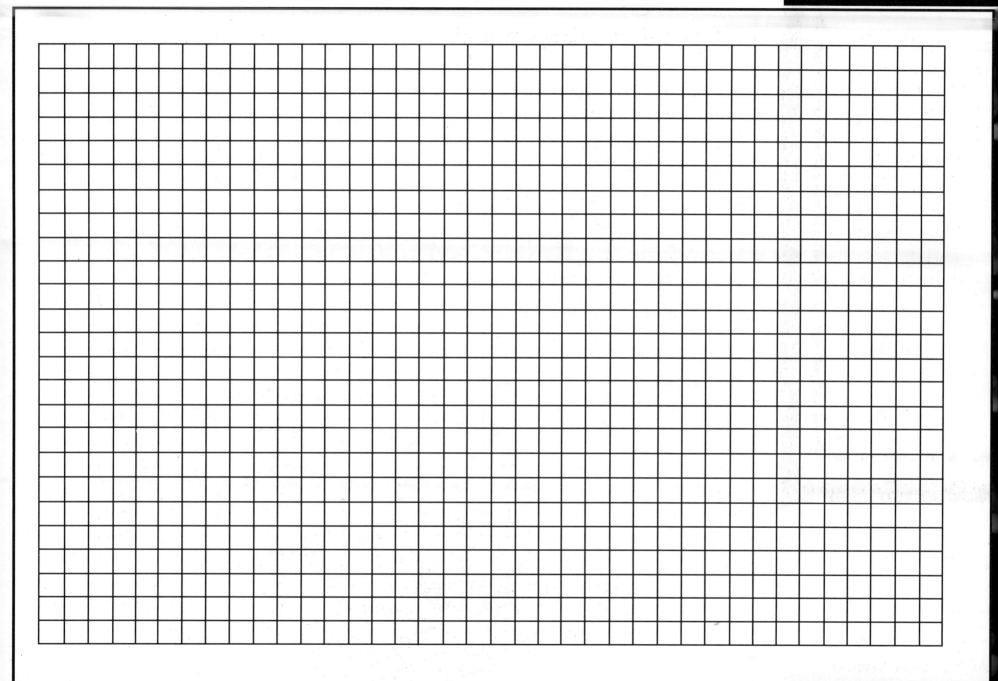

Jumping fractions

YOU WILL NEED: a pencil and someone fairly fit and active to help you!

- First of all jump up and down as many times as you can. Count as you go, and ask your partner to count with you.

- Write down the number of jumps.

- Work out what half that number will be.

- Now your partner must jump up and down that number of times!

- Take it in turns to halve the number and jump until you reach 1.

NOTE: If your number does not divide exactly into halves (for example 31 divides into two 15s and 1 left over) then ignore the remainder.

impact MATHS HOMEWORK

Teachers' Notes
Y E A R   F O U R

The activities in this book also address aspects of the Programme of Study for Number. In particular, this section utilises the following:

• reading, writing and ordering the whole numbers up to 1000, and occasionally beyond;

• estimating to a reasonable degree of accuracy, rounding up and rounding down numbers;

• developing a firm understanding of place value;

• performing addition, subtraction, multiplication and division calculations using a variety of different and appropriate strategies;

• exploring patterns, including sequencing, ordering and matrix patterns;

• consolidating a knowledge of number bonds and tables;

• calculating using fractions or decimals in practical and simple real-life contexts;

• investigating and checking the results of mathematically experimental situations.

Guess away Children can compare their amounts of money. Can they find the average (the mean) by adding up all the amounts on their table and dividing by the number they have? How much do you get if you add all theamount of change in the whole class? Estimate first and then work it out.

Line it up Children can work in pairs to design snakes to make combinations of 100 using the rules of the game. How many different snakes can you find? Who has designed the largest snake?

Five, four, three, two, one Ask the children to compare their scores and the methods they have used. The best follow-up work is to try out different ideas in class, for example: supposing they are only allowed to use + or ÷ and x? What is the lowest number thy can get under these circumstances? Can they display all their attempts in order of the size of the answer?

Making numbers Pairs of children could be given a total to make and each pair could be dealt three cards. Investigate the possible answers. Which are impossible?

Number plates Children could work in pairs using hundreds or tens and units apparatus. They could investigate two numbers which total 501 and this work could be recorded on squared paper.

Card tables This activity focuses on multiplication facts. Chanting the tables out loud is one way to help children to memorise these. Other classroom strategies include: counting through a table in turn - 'Four, eight, twelve ...' and so on; playing 'You're out' in which the children stand in a line and one child standing at the front starts by throwing a multiplication sum at the first child in the line. If they can't answer it straigtaway, they are 'out' and go to the back of the line. If they answer it correctly, they change places with the person at the front, saying 'You're out!'

Coded sums 'Is there more than one solution?' is the first question to ask. What answers have the children come up with? Encourage them to work out some really large and complicated sums by using the code. Perhaps these can be displayed. Can they invent their own codes?

Dice multiplication graph Children will need to work in groups to produce one large graph upon which all their findings are collated. They can then put all these together to produce one enormous class graph. This should give a fairly accurate indication of the probabilities. For example, it should be clear that 12 and 24 are numbers which come up often, and that 9 or 49 are ones which do not. It is then important to discuss these findings. This can lead on to a discussion of factors.

Fair shares Children can play this game in pairs in class, and this time they can formalise the activity by writing down the number they have each time, the number thrown, and then the number of piles and the remainder. They can play the game in groups, using cards and not dice - this will mean that they need a larger pile of counters since they will use numbers up to ten. Can they say how many will be left over without actually sharing the counters?

Five times game Children can play this game in groups, writing down the 'sums' in their maths books as they go. Can they invent a game which will make it more difficult - and involve more skill. For example, you might have to aim for a particular target score and bellowed to use other operations as well as multiplication.

Fizz buzz Clearly this is an excellent game to play as a class. The children have to listen very carefully in order to be ready when their turn comes. They can colour in - or cover with Multilink - the numbers in the three times and five times tables on a 0 - 99 square. What patterns do they make? What about other tables?

Humpty's multiplying wall Children can study and compare each other's walls then make a book or display with collections of walls which have something in common. For example, walls which start with numbers in the two and three times tables, walls with only even numbers ... what patterns can they see? If they are allowed to use a calculator, how large a wall can they make?

Invent a sum Children can make sets of 'sums' which have something in common. These sets may be overlapping, for example the set of sums which are in the four times table, and the set of numbers in the two times table. In the case of some overlapping sets, the intersection may itself prove interesting (two times and three times will give an intersection set of the six times table. Play this game during spare moments.

Multiplying coins Children can work in pairs and use the coins and cards to see how much money they can amass if they keep turning over cards and multiplying that card by a coin of their choice, for example a 50p. How many turns does it take them to get to £50 of £100? They must write down all their turns, and keep a written record.

Multiplying moves Children can discuss their scores. Is there more than one way to reach a particular score? Can some scores only be reached one way? What is the lowest score possible? What is the highest - without moving backwards? Can the children invent another puzzle by re-arranging the numbers? Can they make one with higher numbers?

Pairs Children can collect pairs of cards - or factors - which multiply to give the same number. Thus, how many factors can they fin for 24 or 16? Collect these and make a chart. Which numbers have no factors? Talk about prime and square numbers. Can the children invent a game where they take three cards and multiply them all?

Pebble score Children can invent their own version of this game with different numbers and perhaps more, or less, pebbles. What happens if they start with different numbers of pebbles on the three starting squares? How can they vary the game to make it more exciting?

Pounds and pence Working in groups, the children can collate all the information

they have collected on to one chart. Can they categorise the items they have chosen, for example: edible/non-edible, vegetarian/non-vegetarian, cereal/not cereal and so on. They can then create sets of these items and calculate how much it would cost to buy all the items in one set. How many £1 coins wold you need?

Price factors Children can sort the items they have chosen at home into sets according to price - all those between 10p and 20p in one set, between 20p and 30p in another and so on. They can discuss how much each set would cost in total. How many items are there in each set? What is the averge cost of the items? The children can also compare the prices of different items and talk about value for money. There will also be some formal follow-up work in terms of finding factors of different numbers.

Remainder money Children can play this together in class and write down the sums they do. This will help them to see the remainders that are occurring and to notice any emerging patterns. What is the largest remainder they can get if they throw a six? How about if they throw a four? What is a bad number to throw? Can they say the remainder before they write anything down?

Seven's up Children can practise other divisibility tricks. How do they know if a number is in the three times table (add the digits and if the total is in the three times table, then the larger number is too). How do they know if a number is in the five times table? What about the four times table (halve it - if the answer is even, it is in the four times table).

Treat times Let the children work in groups and talk about the 'treat' they have chosen. How much would it cost to buy ten of their own treat, and ten of their friend's? How much change would they get out of £5? A great deal of arithmetic, written and mental, can arise from this activity.

Tables bingo Children can discuss which numbers come up frequently and which are hard to get. Link this to a discussion about factors. Which numbers have lots of factors? Which ones have very few What do we call numbers which only have themselves and one as factors. Which factor do all even numbers share? Make a display with a number surrounded by its multiples.

Wheel of luck Let the children work in pairs to design a wheel for another pair to use. They can help each other to obtain all the numbers in that wheel - writing down the ways they find. Are some numbers difficult to get? Are any impossible?

Word guess Children can work this game backwards! They can start with a word -

work out the number of each letter, and then calculate how they could get that letter by multiplying two cards. This is not as easy as it sounds. Is it possible to get some letters in more than one way? Are some letters impossible to get? Make a display around each letter with some appropriate definitions of words beginning with that letter, in turn circled by the sums used to make that letter!

Lines of thought Many children really enjoy this game and like to play it again in class. Encourage them to invent their own versions with different coins - or even using numbers rather than coins. A large board with ribbons as lines makes a nice display.

Half his age Children can use this to develop further work on number relationships. For example: if Annie is twice as old as Janet, and there are five years between their ages, how old are they? There are many ways of reformulating this problem - some of them would involve the use of 'x' to stand for an unknown.

Letter count up Children can play the same game using two dice. This increases the amount that they have to subtract. What about making some large initials and using two dice to generate a two-figure number. Can they subtract that in their head? Mental subtraction needs quite specific skills which children need to practise.

Number back and forth Make a class book or a display of the questions that the children think up. Everyone must think up several - and they can be displayed around the number which is the answer. Sometimes leave a question mark so that they have to work it out.

Guess away

- Ask someone to empty the change from their pocket.

- Guess how much is there. Write down your guess.

- Now count it out carefully. Write down how much it was.

- Write a list of the coins and how many of each there were.

- Think of 3 different ways you could make up the same amount using a different handful of coins.

- Write down the 3 ways.

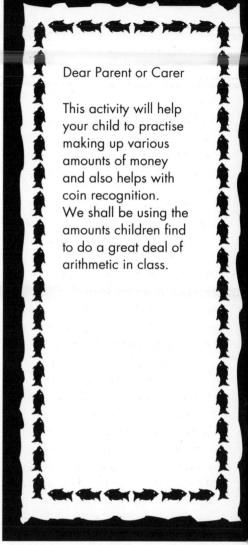

Dear Parent or Carer

This activity will help your child to practise making up various amounts of money and also helps with coin recognition.
We shall be using the amounts children find to do a great deal of arithmetic in class.

_____and

child

_____

helper(s)

_____

did this activity together

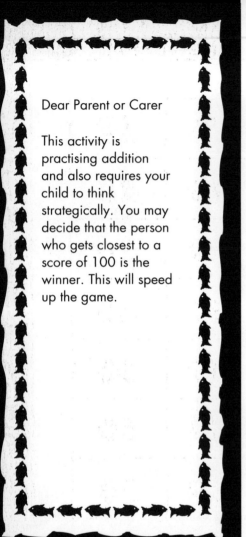

Dear Parent or Carer

This activity is practising addition and also requires your child to think strategically. You may decide that the person who gets closest to a score of 100 is the winner. This will speed up the game.

_____ and
child

_____
helper(s)

_____
did this activity together

Line it up

YOU WILL NEED: a different-coloured counter for each player and coloured felt-tipped pens to match.

● Each place one counter on a number between 0 and 10 on the grid on the accompanying sheet (not both on the same number!).

● Take it in turns to move to a new number which is next to the number you are on - either horizontally, vertically or diagonally.

● Use your coloured felt-tipped pen to draw a line joining the numbers and keep a written running total of the score (adding the numbers of the squares).

● The first to score 100 is the winner!

VARIATIONS
The players' lines may not cross.
Keep the running total in your head.
Can you reach 100 in only 15 turns?
Can you reach 50 in 7 turns?

1	2	3	4	5	6	7	8	9	10
11	12	13	14	15	16	17	18	19	20
21	22	23	24	25	26	27	28	29	30
31	32	33	34	35	36	37	38	39	40
41	42	43	44	45	46	47	48	49	50
51	52	53	54	55	56	57	58	59	60
61	62	63	64	65	66	67	68	69	70
71	72	73	74	75	76	77	78	79	80
81	82	83	84	85	86	87	88	89	90
91	92	93	94	95	96	97	98	99	100

_____and

child

_____

helper(s)

did this activity together

Five, four, three, two, one

YOU WILL NEED: a calculator and a pencil and paper.

● Use the numbers **9 8 7 6 5 4 3 2 1** without changing the order.

● Put in as many +, -, x or ÷ signs as you need in order to finish with as small a number as possible! For example:

98 - 76 - 5 ... and so on.

● Try out several ways to do this. Talk about them. Can you make any of them better?

● Write down your 5 best attempts.

impact MATHS HOMEWORK

Making numbers

YOU WILL NEED: a pack of cards with the face cards removed.

- Deal out 3 cards, face up. For example:

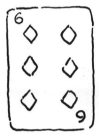  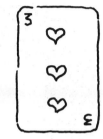

- Make the highest 3-figure number you can. You may not line them up as a 3-digit number (633).

You could line up 2 numbers and multiply by a third.

(63 x 3)

You could add or multiply all 3 numbers.

(6 + 3 + 3) or (6 x 3 x 3)

- Now take another turn with 3 new cards. What is the highest number you can make?

- Try this 5 times.

- Put the numbers in order, highest to lowest.

Dear Parent or Carer

This is an excellent activity for improving multiplication skills. Encourage your child to estimate the answer, for example 63 x 3 is about 180 because three lots of 60 make 180. Check this on the calculator.

_____and
child

_____
helper(s)

_____
did this activity together

_____ and

child

_____

helper(s)

_____

did this activity together

Number plates

● Collect 10 car numbers (digits only).

● Write them in a list with the smallest numbers first and the largest last.

● Each player chooses 2 car numbers to add together. You are looking for 2 which total as near 501 as possible!

● Which of you is closest?

● Try another 2 numbers. How close can you get?

Card tables

YOU WILL NEED: a pack of cards with the face cards removed.

● Lay out all the cards, face down, on the table.

● Turn over any 2 cards.

● If they multiply to make one of the totals in the box, you may keep them.

● If not, turn them back over and leave them in their place.

● Take it in turns to play until there are no pairs left to be taken.

● The player whose cards add up to the highest total is the winner.

6	16	18
10	36	40
40	8	24
30	12	20

Dear Parent or Carer

This activity will help your child to practise multiplication facts. Because the sums will come up in any order, this will test for a random selection of facts rather than simply having to give the answers to a particular table in order.

(five) ... (multiplied by six..)

_____and

child

_____

helper(s)

_____

did this activity together

Coded sums

Each of the symbols below stands for a digit (0, 1, 2, 3, 4, 5, 6, 7, 8 or 9).

$$\neg \qquad \Delta \qquad \S \qquad \P \qquad \circledR$$

$$\dagger \qquad \yen \qquad \varnothing \qquad \Omega \qquad \mu$$

With the help of a partner, find out which is which. Here are some sums to help you. The answers are all correct!

$$\Delta + \yen = \dagger$$

$$\Delta + \varnothing = \circledR$$

$$\S + \Delta + \yen = \P$$

$$\circledR - \Delta - \yen = \neg$$

$$\Omega + \varnothing - \P - \dagger = \neg$$

$$\Delta + \Delta + \Delta + \Delta = \Omega$$

HINT
$\mu = 0$, and Δ and $\neg$ are even numbers!

impact MATHS HOMEWORK

1					
2					
3					
4					
5					
6					
7					
8					
9					
10					
11					
12					
13					
14					
15					
16					
17					
18					
19					
20					
21					
22					
23					
24					
25					
26					
27					
28					
29					
30					
31					
32					
33					
34					
35					
36					

Dice multiplication graph

YOU WILL NEED: a dice and some crayons.

- Each player throws the dice once.

- Multiply the 2 numbers together.

- Shade a square in the row next to that number.

- Continue to play and shade squares in the appropriate rows.

- Throw the dice at least 30 times.

- Which rows have most squares shaded?

- Which rows have no squares shaded?

- Can you say why this is?

Dear Parent or Carer

This activity not only helps to practise multiplication skills and teach number facts, but it also requires children to think about which numbers have more factors and are, therefore, likely to crop up more often.

_____and

child

_____

helper(s)

_____

did this activity together

Fair shares

YOU WILL NEED: a handful of counters for each player (dried peas/beans or pasta would do) and a dice.

● Throw the dice.

● Divide your counters into the number of piles shown on the dice. (If you throw a 5, share out your counters into 5 little heaps.)

● Put any that are left over on to a central pile.

● Take it in turns to play. The first player with no counters left is the winner.

HINT: If you want to speed up the game, you can agree that if one player has no counters left over for 2 turns in a row, on the third turn they may discard one on to the central pile before throwing the dice.

Five times game

YOU WILL NEED: a dice and a pencil and paper for each player.

● Throw the dice 5 times.

● Write down the numbers then cross out any 2s or 5s.

✗ 3 4 ✗ 6

● Multiply the remaining numbers. For example:

3 x 4 x 6 = 72

● Throw the dice again - the number of times you throw it depends upon the numbers not crossed out! (In this case 3 times.)

● Write down the numbers you throw, and cross out any 2s or 5s.

● Multiply the numbers left, as before.

● Continue to play until you have only one number left not crossed out.

● Take 5 turns each and then add your scores together for each turn. Highest score wins.

Dear Parent or Carer

Your child will need to do a large number of sums in the course of this activity. The more sums the more fun it will be. Perhaps if there are not many of you playing you can persuade teddy or the cat to play as well! Who will do teddy's sums for him?

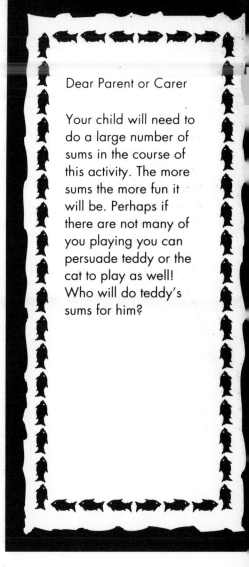

_____and

child

_____

helper(s)

_____

did this activity together

_____and

child

_____

helper(s)

_____

did this activity together

Fizz Buzz

The more people that play this game, the more fun it is!

● Take it in turns to count out loud starting at 1. Each person says one number.

BUT if the number you have to say is in the 3 times table, you say 'FIZZ' instead of the number. The person after you has to say the next number as if you had said your number as normal.

OR if the number you have to say is in the 5 times table, you say 'BUZZ' instead.

For example: 'one', 'two', 'FIZZ', 'four', 'BUZZ', 'FIZZ', 'seven', 'eight'… and so on.

If the number appears in both tables you say 'FIZZ BUZZ'!

● Can you get to 100 without making any mistakes?

Humpty's multiplying wall

YOU WILL NEED: a pencil; some paper and a calculator.

You are going to build a wall for Humpty Dumpty!

● The number on each brick can be worked out by multiplying the numbers on the 2 bricks below it. You will need to write in the numbers along the bottom row to start you off. See the example below.

● How high a wall can you build?

● Can you build a symmetrical wall?

● What happens if the bottom row of bricks all have the same number?

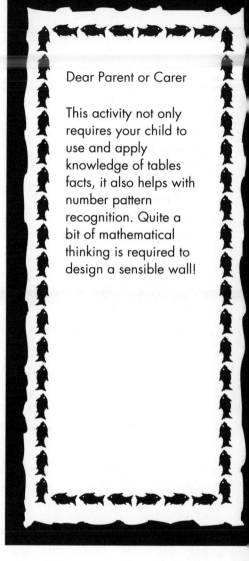

Dear Parent or Carer

This activity not only requires your child to use and apply knowledge of tables facts, it also helps with number pattern recognition. Quite a bit of mathematical thinking is required to design a sensible wall!

_____and

child

_____

helper(s)

_____

did this activity together

Invent a sum

YOU WILL NEED: a calculator to check your answers!

● Choose 2 numbers smaller than 10 and multiply them together. For example:

6 x 4 = ?

Have a guess!

● Use a calculator to check your answer. Were you right?

● Now let your partner choose 2 numbers to multiply.

● Score 5 points for every correct answer, 3 points if your guess is 1 either side, and 1 point if it is within 2 of the right answer!

● Take 5 turns each and then add up your scores. Highest score wins.

● If this is too easy, try with one of the numbers bigger than 10 and one smaller.

Multiplying coins

YOU WILL NEED: a bag; a pack of cards; a pencil and paper for each player and at least 2 of each of the following coins – 1p, 2p, 5p, 10p.

● Put all the coins into a bag and the cards, face down, in a pile.

● Take a card and a coin.

● Place the card, face up, with the coin on top of it.

● Now write down how much you would have if you multiplied the number on your card by the value of your coin. This is your score. For example:

2p on a 7   **7 x 2 = 14**   **= 14p**

● If you take a face card (a K or a Q or a J) you must subtract 10p from your total score.

● Take it in turns to play. The first player to reach £3.33 is the winner!

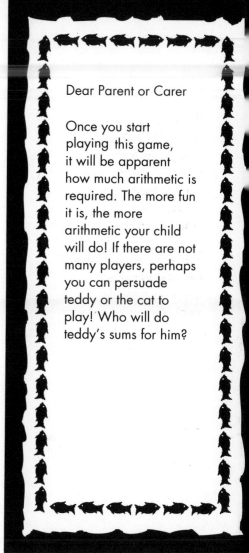

Dear Parent or Carer

Once you start playing this game, it will be apparent how much arithmetic is required. The more fun it is, the more arithmetic your child will do! If there are not many players, perhaps you can persuade teddy or the cat to play! Who will do teddy's sums for him?

_____and

child

_____

helper(s)

_____

did this activity together

Multiplying moves

YOU WILL NEED: 8 counters to fit the squares on the grid (7 in one colour and 1 in a different colour).

● Place the counters on the grid, covering every number except the 8 with the odd coloured counter on the 2.

> The aim is to move the odd counter from the 2 to the 8. You can only do this by moving the counter on to adjacent empty squares. Any counter can be moved up or down to an adjacent empty square to make space.

2	9	4
7	5	3
6	1	8

● Every time you move a counter, you multiply the number on the square it moves from by the number on the square it moves to. This is your score.

● Keep adding your scores till you have succeeded in moving the odd counter on to the 8!

● Try this several times. What is your highest score? What is your lowest?

impact MATHS HOMEWORK

Pairs

YOU WILL NEED: a pack of cards with the face cards removed.

The aim of this game is to collect pairs of cards.

● Deal 5 cards to each player. Place the rest in a pile, face down.

● You can make a pair by placing 2 of your cards, face up, in front of you, providing that the 2 numbers multiply to make one of the following totals:

6   8   10   12   16   18   20

24   30   36   40   49

● If 1 player places a pair in front of them, another may take it if they can make the same answer using a pair of their own.

They can now place all 4 cards, face up, in front of them.

> Suppose you have 4 and 9 in front of you. Another player has a 6 and a 6 in their hand. They can take your 4 and your 9 and place both pairs, face up, in front of them.
>
> These 2 pairs can both be taken by any player who can produce a pair which also multiplies to that number.

● Take it in turns to play. If you can't make a pair then take a card from the central pile.

● When all the cards are gone, the player with the most pairs is the winner.

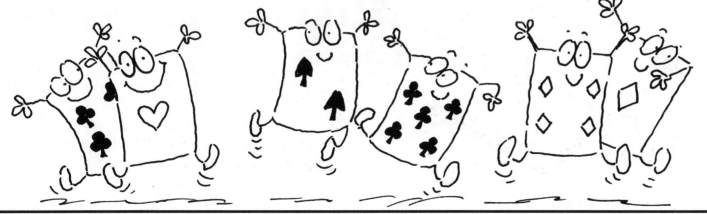

Dear Parent or Carer

This activity looks at multiplication facts and also at which pairs of factors multiply to make the same product (for example 2 x 6 = 3 x 4). The more children enjoy the game, the more practice they will do without noticing it!

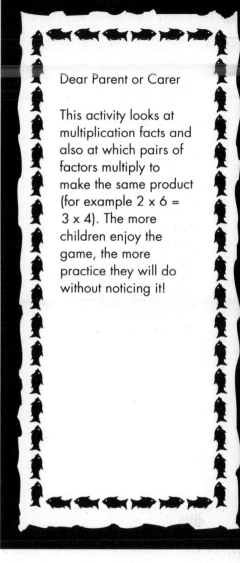

_____and

child

_____

helper(s)

_____

did this activity together

Pebble score

YOU WILL NEED: counters, such as pebbles, dried peas, beans, uncooked pasta or small bricks and a grid like the one below.

● Place 3 pebbles on each of the squares x9, x6 and x8 on the grid.

● Take it in turns to pick up all the pebbles on any one square and then move in a clockwise direction, dropping off a pebble at each square passed.

● You score the number of the last square on which a pebble is dropped, multiplied by the number of pebbles on that square. So:

If you start by picking up the 3 pebbles on x6, you move round, dropping 1 on x7, 1 on x2 and the last 1 on x9. There are now 4 pebbles on x9 so you score $4 \times 9 = 36$.

● Add up your scores each turn. The first player to reach 99 is the winner!

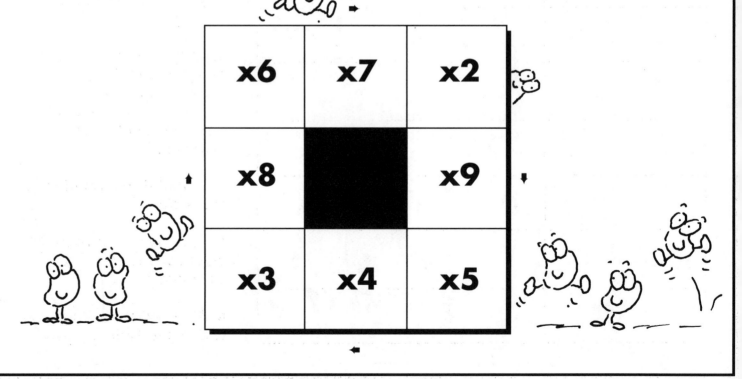

food	price	number of 10ps	change

Pounds and pence

● Imagine that you have 10p coins and no other money.

● Choose 10 items of food and find their real price. (Look in your food cupboard or make a note next time you're out shopping.)

● Write this information in the table.

● How many 10p coins would you need to buy each item?

● Work out the change you would get. Write it down.

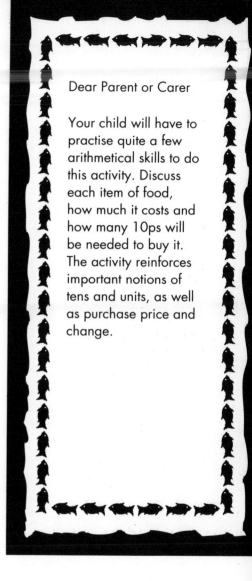

Dear Parent or Carer

Your child will have to practise quite a few arithmetical skills to do this activity. Discuss each item of food, how much it costs and how many 10ps will be needed to buy it. The activity reinforces important notions of tens and units, as well as purchase price and change.

_____and

child

_____

helper(s)

_____

did this activity together

_____and

child

_____

helper(s)

_____

did this activity together

Price factors

● Look in your store cupboard and find 3 things which have prices on them. Write down the prices. For example:

● Write down the factors of each price. (Factors are the numbers which divide into another number without leaving a remainder.)

● These can be used to make factor trees as in the diagram below. Use your calculator to help you check they work.

● Now complete the factor trees below.

● Now make up your own factor trees

impact MATHS HOMEWORK

Remainder money

YOU WILL NEED: a pack of cards with the face cards removed; a handful of change; a dice and a pencil and paper for each player.

● Place the cards in a pile, face down, and the money within easy reach.

● Take 2 cards from the pile and make them into a 2-digit number.

If you take 2 and 7
You can make 27 or 72.

● Throw the dice and divide the number thrown into 1 of the 2-digit numbers.

If you throw a 6 you could do:
27 ÷ 6 = 4 (remainder 3)
or 72 ÷ 6 = 12 (remainder 0).

● Choose which sum you are going to use. The remainder is your score for that turn and you may take that amount of money from the pile.

If you choose 27 ÷ 6 = 4 (remainder 3)
Take 3p from the pile.

● Take it in turns to play.

● The first person to reach 20p is the winner.

Dear Parent or Carer

This activity will help your child to practise division and addition skills. A surprising number of sums will be required – especially if you make the game fun and play several times over the weekend!

_____and
child

_____
helper(s)

_____

did this activity together

_____and

child

_____

helper(s)

_____

did this activity together

Seven's up

How do we know if a big number is in the 7 times table?

Try this trick.

● Take a number. For example:

98

● Multiply the units by 5:

8 x 5 = 40

● Add the answer to the number of tens:

40 + 9 = 49

● If that number is in the 7 times table, then the bigger number is too!

● Try 175.

● Now try some of your own!

impact MATHS HOMEWORK

Treat times

● Choose a chocolate bar or a packet of snacks which you really like!

● Write down its price.

● Talk to someone about how much it would cost to buy 5 of your friends 1 each.

Don't use a calculator!

```
HINT: Try 10 friends first! It's easier.
```

● Work out what it would cost to buy 1 for every person in your class at school.

```
HINT: Try working in 10s again:
10 friends, 20 friends . . . and so on.
```

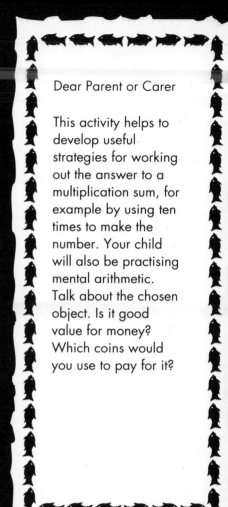

Dear Parent or Carer

This activity helps to develop useful strategies for working out the answer to a multiplication sum, for example by using ten times to make the number. Your child will also be practising mental arithmetic. Talk about the chosen object. Is it good value for money? Which coins would you use to pay for it?

_____and

child

_____

helper(s)

_____

did this activity together

Tables bingo

YOU WILL NEED: a pack of cards; some counters in different colours (1 colour for each player) and the board on the accompanying sheet.

● Place the cards in a pile, face down.

● Pick up 2 cards.

● Multiply the numbers on the cards together and place a counter on that number on the grid. If you cannot do so, replace the cards at the bottom of the pile.

● Take it in turns. The first person to get 3 of their counters in a row, in any direction, is the winner.

2	54	30	15	10	14	9	50
56	24	64	12	32	40	56	36
25	6	14	2	63	24	28	16
4	10	16	18	48	36	40	35
9	8	20	24	8	3	18	27
1	24	4	30	36	12	20	48
49	15	16	9	40	48	32	45
64	72	21	6	7	60	30	42

Wheel of luck

YOU WILL NEED: a dice and a different coloured crayon for each player.

● Choose 16 numbers between 1 and 50 and write them in the spaces on the board on the accompanying sheet.

● Throw the dice 3 times.

● Use the numbers thrown in any way you like (add, subtract, divide or multiply). If you can make one of the numbers on the wheel, you may colour it in.

● Take it in turns to throw the dice. The player who colours in most numbers on the wheel is the winner.

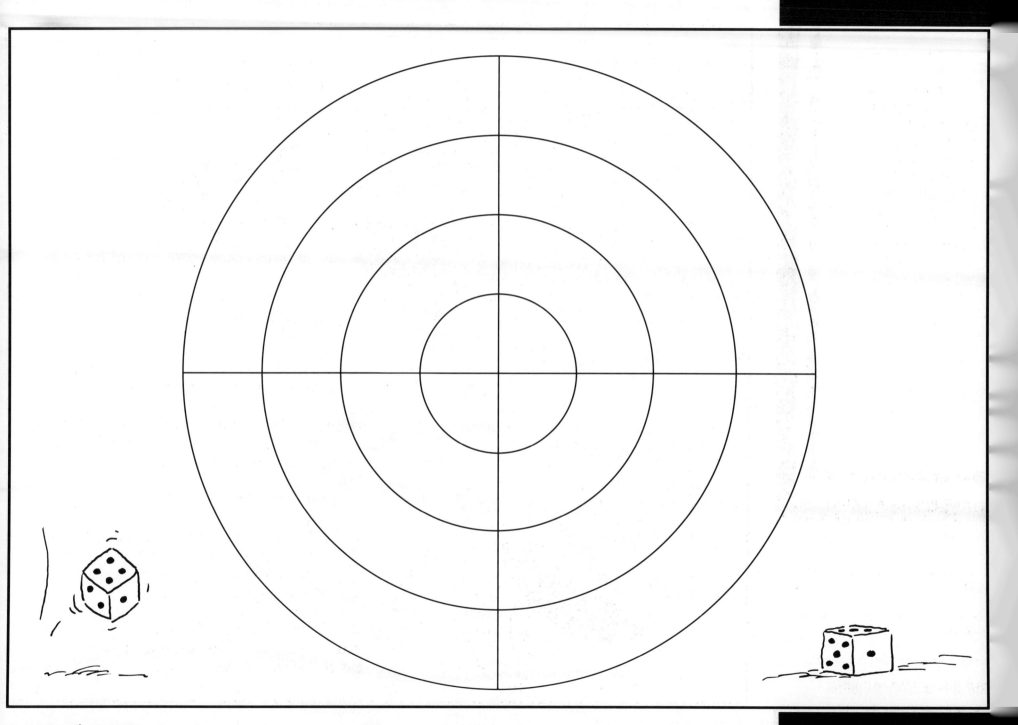

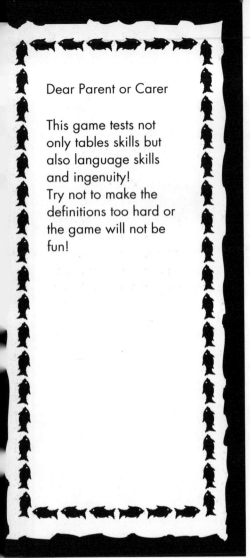
Word guess

YOU WILL NEED: a pack of cards and a small dictionary.

● Place the pile of cards, face down, on the table.

● Choose 2 cards. (Don't show them to your partner).

● Multiply the values. If the total is more than 26, add the digits together. For example:

7 x 8 = 56

5 + 6 = 11

● Turn to that letter of the alphabet in the dictionary.

11th letter is K

● Give your partner the definition of a word beginning with that letter. Can they guess the word?

In this case you might say:

'Something you use to boil the water for tea.'

● Take 5 turns each. Score 1 point for each word you get right. The player with the highest score is the winner.

impact MATHS HOMEWORK

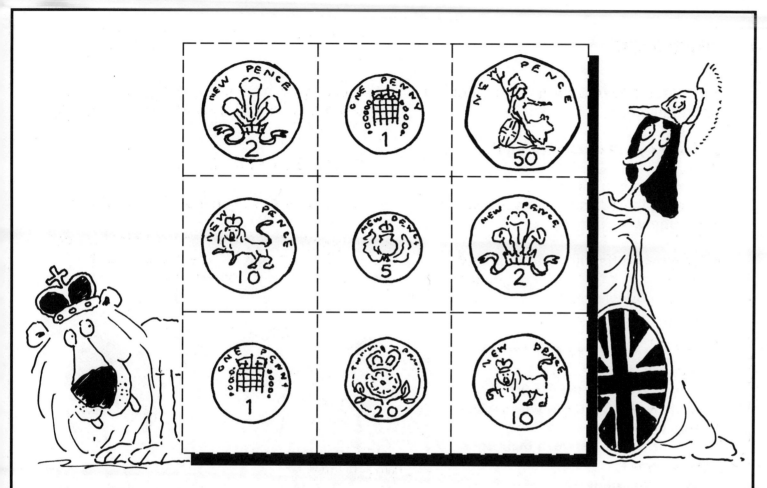

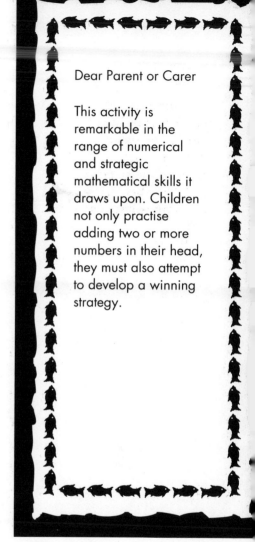

Dear Parent or Carer

This activity is remarkable in the range of numerical and strategic mathematical skills it draws upon. Children not only practise adding two or more numbers in their head, they must also attempt to develop a winning strategy.

Lines of thought

YOU WILL NEED: a pencil.

● Take it in turns to draw straight lines through the coins in the diagram.

● Each line must pass through at least 2 coins.

● No line may be the same as one already drawn.

● Add up the values of the coins you draw through as you go.

● The first player to reach £3.99 is the winner!

_____and
child

_____
helper(s)

_____
did this activity together

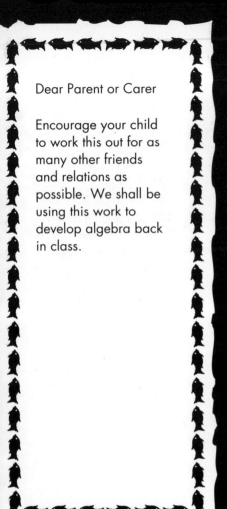

_____and

child

_____

helper(s)

_____

did this activity together

Half his age

● Choose someone older than you in your family.

When will you be half their age?

● To do this you must first work out the difference in your ages. How old were they when you were born?

● Take that difference and double it.

● This is how old they will be when you are half their age. For example:

> **Wilf is 8**
> **Harry (Wilf's brother) is 20**
> **Harry was 12 (20 - 8) when Wilf was born**
> **The difference between their ages is 12 years**
> **So, when Wilf is 12**
> **Harry will be 24 (12 x 2).**
> **Wilf will be half his age.**

● Do this for as many people as you can.

● You could choose someone younger than you and work out when they will be half your age!

impact MATHS HOMEWORK

Letter count up

- Draw your initials in large letters.

- Now find some small dried pasta pieces or small Lego bricks or small buttons or raisins and lay them in a line along your initials.

- Before you do this guess how many will fit. Write down your guess.

- Lay the pieces along the letters and count them. Write down your answer.

- Now play this game.

- Take it in turns to throw a dice and remove that number of pieces from the letters.

- Say how many are left. Your partner must check whether you are right. If you are you can keep the pieces you took. If you are wrong you must put the pieces back.

- Now let your partner take a turn and you must check their answer.

- Keep playing until all the pieces are gone. The player with the most pieces is the winner.

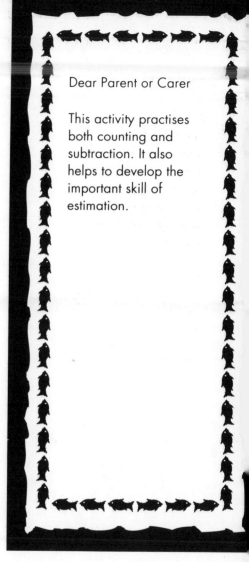

Dear Parent or Carer

This activity practises both counting and subtraction. It also helps to develop the important skill of estimation.

_____and

child

_____

helper(s)

_____

did this activity together

impact MATHS HOMEWORK

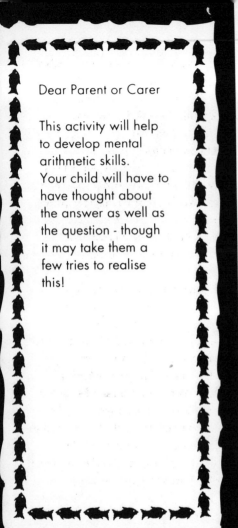
_____and
child

_____
helper(s)

_____
did this activity together

Number back and forth

YOU WILL NEED: a handful of coins.

● Think of a number. Don't say it out loud!

● Ask your partner a question to which the answer is your number. For example:

Your number is 80
So the question you ask is
'What number am I if I am 4 times 20?'

● If they reply correctly they can take a coin.

● They then give you a question. If you guess their number correctly, you take a coin.

● Take it in turns until all the coins are gone. The player with the most coins is the winner.

impact MATHS HOMEWORK

Teachers' Notes

YEAR FIVE

The activities in this book also address aspects of the Programme of Study for Number. In particular, this section utilises the following skills:

- counting, reading, writing and ordering the whole numbers up to 1000 and decimal numbers in the context of money;
- using their understanding of place value to perform calculations and solve problems;
- performing simple and complex calculations in addition, subtraction, multiplication and division;
- exploring and interpreting patterns;
- consolidating number facts, including number bonds and tables;
- using more complex fractions, and
- understanding and using the relationship between the operations.

Area multiplication Children can formalise this work in their maths books by doing several sums. They can start to perform the calculation without having to do the drawing if they can 'imagine' the rectangle. It is also worth trying this with one or two very large rectangles, asking the children to draw them out on squared paper and display them.

Digit sums Children can work in groups to compare their results. Which numbers

have they found? Some groups will find it stimulating to extend the activity and work on much larger numbers. Can they find any patterns? Other groups of children may work on the patterns obtained by adding the digits, for example: suppose they add the digits of each of the numbers in the three times table. What pattern do they find? How about other times tables?

Multiplication made easy Children will be very impressed by a method of multiplication which does not require tables! Let them make two really large sums in this way to display and discuss. Can

they get some idea of why it works by thinking about the doubling, i.e. 52 = 2 x 26, 208 = 8 x 26 - and so on. How many times 26 do we need?

Jumping divisions This activity helps children to learn their tables and it can, and should be followed by rehearsed tables practice. Some children will learn these number facts by remembering the 'sing-song' of the recitation, others will

grasp the patterns and others will visualise them on a page. A variety of approaches will maximise their chances of learning these facts.

Invent a hard sum This activity can lead into ways of checking more difficult multiplication sums. Children can learn to multiply first of all by the tens digit and then by the units. It is helpful to practise quick mental multiplication skills - getting children to double numbers, and double them again, asking them to add numbers in their heads and so on. A display of some of the children's really hard sums can be fun.

Magic squares Children can show each other their magic squares and this activity can lead to a wonderful 'class book' or display. Did anyone find a three by three square? They can work on this in class. Can they find symmetrical variations of those already discovered (this may be a useful activity for those who did not do this at home - or for pupils who find this difficult).

Number economy Children can work in groups to collate their findings. How many ways have they found of making each number? Are there any more ways of making seven, for example? Can they sort their 'ways' into sets under each number and then display these? Perhaps different groups can work on different numbrs. Some children, working individually or in groups, may like to try out what happens when the number thief leaves only even numbers.

Multiplying phone numbers Children can work in groups and check each other's phone numbers. They can try to discover if their estimation skills have improved. Can

they guess the answers to a phone number which looks similar to their own? Does it make any difference in which order the numbers are multiplied? Try the same activity with car numbers.

Car multiplications Discuss the children's findings. Why does the activity work? would it work with larger numbers? What happens if one of the number plates has a zero in it? Can they try the same thing using three number plates? Display some of the larger sums for class discussion!

Fraction pattern Children can have great fun in class designing their own fraction pattern. This is harder than it looks and introduces a great deal of number and shape work since they will have to calculate the precise fractions which it is possible to colour. Good ones take a lot of work but make a lovely display!

Fraction chances This activity can lead to a great deal of work on fractions. An extension of the game can involve throwing the two dice and finding the fraction

Twenty Seven!

obtained as a quantity of a specified amount (for example 60). Children can take three turns each (writing down the sums) and the person with the highet score at the end is the winner.

Get there first This activity leads into some nice work on number series of this type. Start with the number one and two and generate the Fibonacci sequence. Look at every third number. Look at every fifth number. What other patterns can be seen? What patterns emerge if the starting numbers are both even? What if they are both odd? What if they are both the same?

Layabouts Collect pairs of cards and work out their products. How many pairs are there with a product of 12? How many with a product of nine? Why are some products easier to find than others? Talk about factors and perhaps make a display of all the pairs which make a particular product.

Sun magic When the children bring their work back into class encourage them to compare their findings. Which rectangles have they tried? Did anyone find one that did not work? What is the relationship betwen the numbers in a number square - vertically/horizontally?

Making multiples Children can try playing this game in class and should write down the combinations of seven that they find. How many different combinations of seven has the class come up with? Keep a display of all the different ways you discover. How will you know when you have them all?

Score 27 This activity is best followed up by collecting all the ways of making 27 that have been found on one display board. On another you could collect all the five card line-ups which cannot make 27. Encourage the children to work on the 'impossible' line-ups during spare moments - it is surprising how many turn out to be possible after all!

Small fortune Children can play this game in pairs and write down all their card pairs and their products. How many sums do they do? Play the same game with the whole class by asking them to write down six numbers that are products on a piece of paper. The teacher then turns over two cards at a time. If the children have written the product of those two cards on their list, they may cross it out. The first person to cross out all their products wins.

Point the way Children can use a pack of cards to create their own one-place decimal numbers in their maths book. When they have three or four numbers, can

they add them up? What numbers do they make? Use a calculator to check their answers are correct. This can be played as a game by saying that the person with the score nearest ten at the end is the winner!

Number test Children can play a game in class which involves writing numbers and reading them. They can play in pairs with a one minute timer. One child gives his partner a starting number between 10,000 and 50,000 then turns over the timer and shouts 'Start!'. The second child must write the numbers in order starting at their chosen number as fast as they can. When the timer has run through, the first child calls 'Stop!'. The second child then says the number they have written out loud: Thirty-three thousand, four hundred and sixty-seven. The first child must, without looking write the number down in figures. They then compare numbers and, if they match, they may swap places and take another turn. Can they get three numbers to match?

Ginormous numbers Children can practise writing big numbers in class by working together in a group and ordering all their ginormous numbers from smallest to largest. They can make displays of their lists. Can they do some ginormous addition sums? Or even subtractions?

Card race Children can work together in groups to play this game. Lay down a card, face up, and then deal out four cards to each member of the group. How many ways can they all find to make the number of the card in the middle? Can they write

them all down? Display as many 'ways' as you can using a card in the middle and drawing all the sums in bright colous around it!

One million words Are the children's books all about the same size? Have they taken any notice of the area of a page? Extension work could involve estimating how many words there are in the Bible then checking, or finding other examples of 1,000,000 words.

Are you square? Can all the even numbers between 2 and 50 be made using these square numbers?Put together the work done at home and find out if this is so. Can some numbers be made in more than one way? Suppose you want to make the next set of even numbers - from 50 to 100. Which square numbers would you need to add to your bag?

Area multiplication

YOU WILL NEED: squared paper.

Here's an easy way to multiply 2 big numbers. For example:

27 x 16

● On your squared paper draw a rectangle 27 squares by 16.

● Mark off the tens and units.

27 = 20 + 7 and **16 = 10 + 6**

Now we have 4 rectangles:
A B C and D

A = 20 x 10	**= 200**	
B = 7 x 10	**= 70**	
C = 6 x 20	**= 120**	
D = 7 x 6	**= 42**	

TOTAL   **432**

● Try this with 2 numbers of your own.

● Does it work with other numbers?

● Show someone how it works.

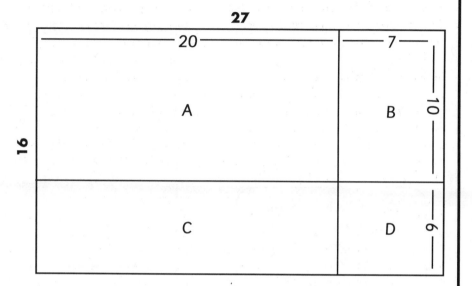

Dear Parent or Carer

This activity introduces the idea of long multiplication. It also reinforces the concepts of hundreds, tens and units, which are so important as the arithmetic gets harder.

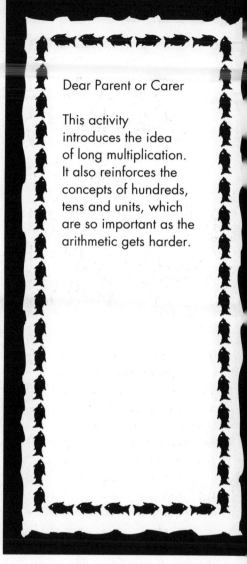

_____and

child

_____

helper(s)

_____

did this activity together

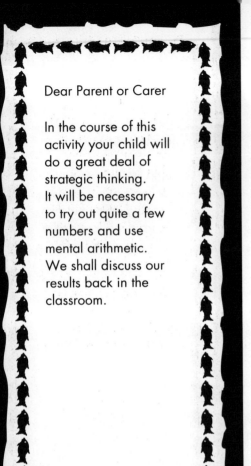

_____and

child

_____

helper(s)

_____

did this activity together

Digit sums

18 is a special number. It is twice the sum of its own digits.

Its digits are 1 and 8.

1 + 8 = 9

2 × 9 = 18

One number under 50 is 3 times the sum of its digits. Can you work out which number it is?

_____

4 numbers under 50 are 4 times the sum of their digits. Try to find them all.

_____

Can you find the only number which is 5 times the sum of its digits? (This is still under 50.)

_____

What about the only number which is 6 times its digits? (Over 50 this time.)

_____

Can you predict which numbers would be 7, 8 and 9 times the sum of their own digits?

_____

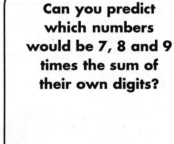

impact MATHS HOMEWORK

Multiplication made easy

Try this new way of multiplying big numbers.
You don't even need to know your tables!

For example: 26 x 19.

Double		26	and halve	19
the			the	
number		52	number on	9
on the		104	the right	4
left		208	(leave out	2
		416	any spare	1
			numbers)	

Keep going till the right-hand column reaches 1.

● Cross out any rows with an even
number in the right-hand column
then add up the remaining numbers
in the left-hand column.

26	19
52	9
~~104~~	~~4~~
~~208~~	~~2~~
416	1
494	

● Check your answer using a calculator.

● Try again with 2 other numbers!

Dear Parent or Carer

This activity is perfect for making children (and adults!) think about why numbers work as they do. Some children will be fascinated by the fact that the method works at all. Encourage your child to try lots of different numbers, and to puzzle out why it might work (Hint: Think about *doubling*.)

_____and

child

_____

helper(s)

_____

did this activity together

_____and
child

_____
helper(s)

_____
did this activity together

Jumping divisions

YOU WILL NEED: a counter for each player; a dice and the track on the accompanying page.

● Place your counters at the start of the track.

● Take it in turns to throw the dice and move your counter along the line to the next number which is a multiple of the number thrown. For example:

If you throw a 5, and you are already on 6, move to 10 (because 10 is the next number in the 5 times table).

If you don't know whether your number divides into the number thrown check by jumping up and down!

So to check if 16 divides by 4, jump in 4s up to 16, holding up 1 finger for every 4 jumps!

The first player to reach 30 is the winner.

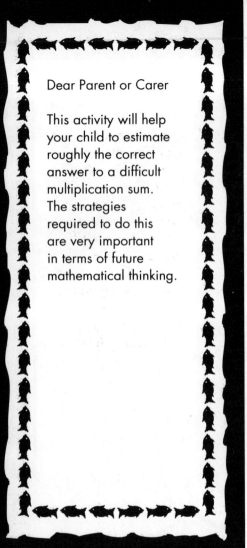

_____and

child

_____

helper(s)

_____

did this activity together

Invent a hard sum

YOU WILL NEED: a calculator to check your answers!

● Choose 2 numbers for your partner.

● They must guess what the answer will be if they are multiplied together. For example:

16 x 4 = ?

HAVE A GUESS!

● Use a calculator to check their answer.

● They score the difference between their answer and the answer on the calculator! Write down their score.

● Now ask your partner to choose 2 numbers and you take a turn at guessing.

● Take 5 turns each then add up your scores – lowest score wins.

(It is important to be able to estimate so give praise for being nearly right.)

impact MATHS HOMEWORK

Magic squares

A magic square usually looks something like this.

2	9	4
7	5	3
6	1	8

Each row and each column add up to 15.

Does each row and each column multiply to the same number?

● Can you create a MULTIPLYING magic square with only 4 numbers? (Use the empty square.)

● If you feel brave you could try a 3 x 3 square but we're not sure if this is possible!

Dear Parent or Carer

This activity is very demanding in terms of logical mathematical thinking. Your child will begin by adopting a 'trial and error' approach but will quickly start to develop a more strategic line of enquiry. At the same time, of course, this helps to practise multiplication facts.

_____and

child

_____

helper(s)

_____

did this activity together

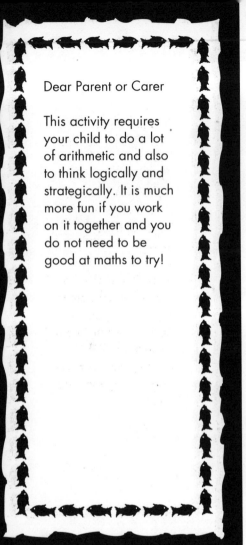

_____and

child

_____

helper(s)

_____

did this activity together

Number economy

A number thief has stolen all the numbers in the world except 3, 5 and 9!

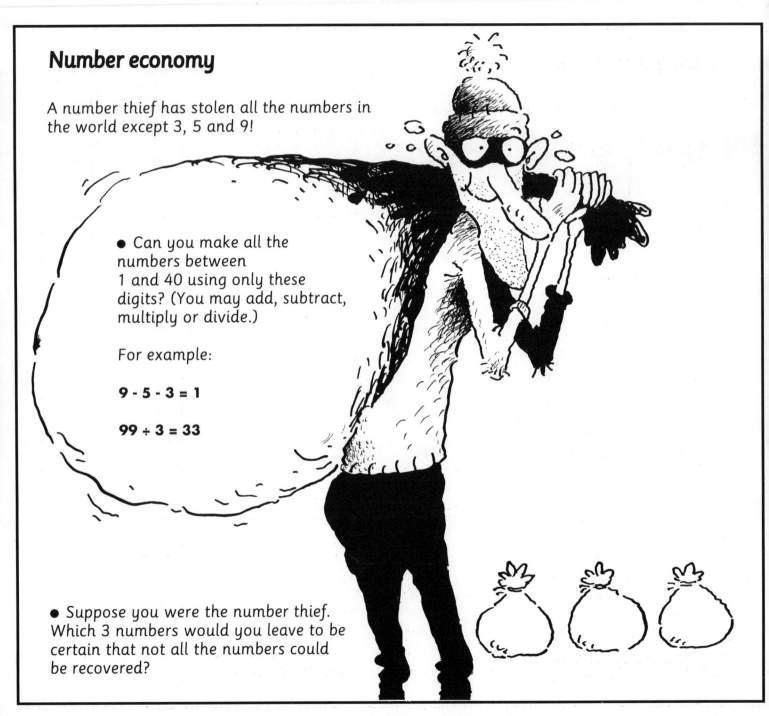

● Can you make all the numbers between 1 and 40 using only these digits? (You may add, subtract, multiply or divide.)

For example:

9 - 5 - 3 = 1

99 ÷ 3 = 33

● Suppose you were the number thief. Which 3 numbers would you leave to be certain that not all the numbers could be recovered?

impact MATHS HOMEWORK

Multiplying phone numbers

YOU WILL NEED: a calculator and a pencil.

● Write down your phone number. (If you don't have a phone, use a friend's number!)

● Ask everyone in your family to guess what the answer will be if you multiply all the digits, ignoring any zeros!

● Write down their guesses in the chart opposite.

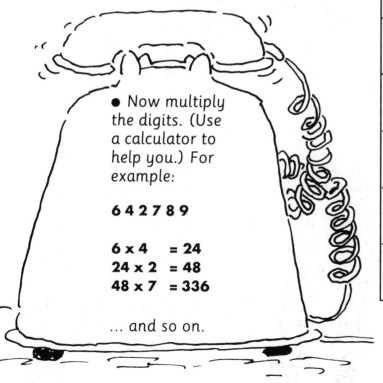

● Now multiply the digits. (Use a calculator to help you.) For example:

6 4 2 7 8 9

6 x 4   = 24
24 x 2 = 48
48 x 7 = 336

... and so on.

Person	Guess

● Who was the closest? How far out was their guess?

Dear Parent or Carer

This activity is excellent for helping children (and adults!) estimate the answer to a problem. Estimation is an extremely important skill in modern life.
We often need an approximation of an answer to be able to make a judgement about whether to buy something or if it will fit. It will also help to practise arithmetic skills.

_____and

child

_____

helper(s)

_____

did this activity together

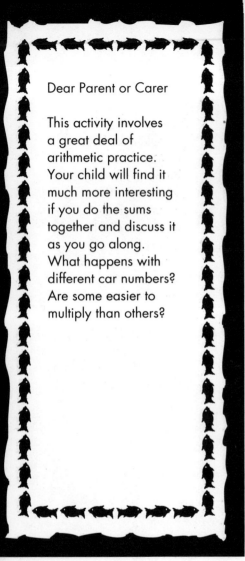

Car multiplications

● Collect the numbers from 2 car number plates (3 digits) and write them down. For example:

9 8 1

3 7 2

F981 TBC

E372 UV2

● Multiply each vertical column and write the answers underneath.

<u>9</u>	<u>8</u>	<u>1</u>	9 x 3 = 27
<u>3</u>	<u>7</u>	<u>2</u>	8 x 7 = 56
27	56	2	1 x 2 = 2

● Using a calculator, if you need it, multiply each horizontal row and write the answers at the side.

<u>9</u>	<u>8</u>	<u>1</u>	**72** (9 x 8 = 72 x 1 = 72)
<u>3</u>	<u>7</u>	<u>2</u>	**42** (3 x 7 = 21 x 2 = 42)
27	56	2	

● Use your calculator to check that the bottom 3 numbers multiplied together equal the product of the 2 side numbers.

27 x 56 = 1512 x 2 = 3024

72 x 42 = 3024

● Try other pairs of car number plates.

impact MATHS HOMEWORK

Fraction pattern

● Colour in this pattern using the colours red, green and blue.

● Discuss with your partner what fraction of your pattern is red and what fraction is blue. Is more of your pattern red or blue?

● Is the fraction covered by 2 of your colours greater than, less than, or about the same as half?

● Make up a new pattern for someone else to try.

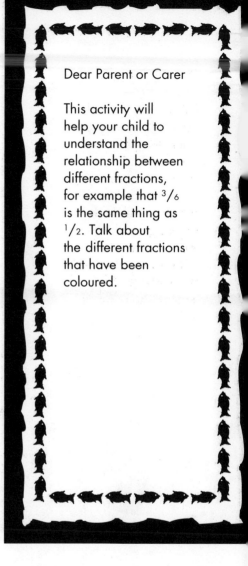

Dear Parent or Carer

This activity will help your child to understand the relationship between different fractions, for example that $3/6$ is the same thing as $1/2$. Talk about the different fractions that have been coloured.

_____and

child

_____

helper(s)

_____

did this activity together

_____and

child

_____

helper(s)

_____

did this activity together

Fraction chances

YOU WILL NEED: a dice; a pencil and paper.

● Throw the dice twice.

● Use the 2 numbers to make a fraction less than 1, as shown under the dice below.

● If you throw 2 numbers the same, throw the dice a third time to get 2 different numbers.

● Write down your fraction.

● Take it in turns to play.

● The first player to be able to make 1 exactly using any of the fractions they have written down is the winner for that game.

● Play 5 games. Best of 5 wins!

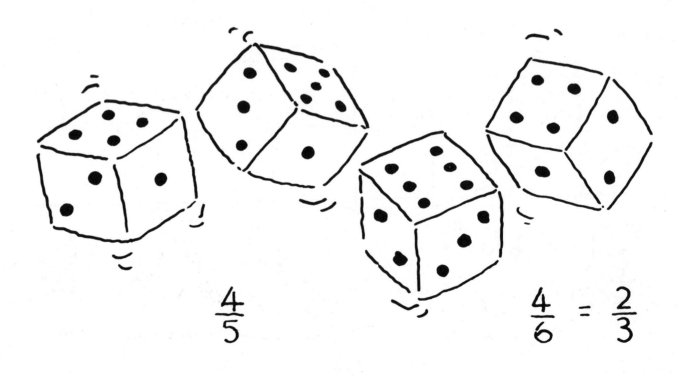

$$\frac{4}{5}$$

$$\frac{4}{6} = \frac{2}{3}$$

impact MATHS HOMEWORK

Get there first

YOU WILL NEED: a pencil and paper and lots of patience!

● Ask your partner to think of 2 numbers (both under 10).

● Ask them to add these 2 numbers together, then add the last of the 2 numbers to the total of those 2 numbers. This makes a fourth number. For example:

They choose 2 and 4.

2 + 4 = 6   then   **4 + 6 = 10**

● They now have a series: 2, 4, 6, 10. Add the 6 and 10 to get a fifth number: 16. Continue this till they get a seventh number.

● They must tell you their 7th number.

● You can now tell them immediately what the first 10 numbers in the series will add up to. (You do this by multiplying their seventh number by 11!)

● They then work out the next 3 numbers in the series.

2 4 6 10 16 26 42 68 110 178
                                7th   10th
(11 x 42 = 462)

● Now add them all up.

Answer = 462

● Try this with different pairs of starting numbers.

Why do you think it works?

Dear Parent or Carer

This activity can be great fun, especially if it is treated as a trick! Your child will need to do a lot of mental arithmetic and will be intrigued as to why it works! Any ideas?

_____and
child

_____
helper(s)

_____
did this activity together

_____and

child

_____

helper(s)

_____

did this activity together

Layabouts

YOU WILL NEED: a pack of cards with the face cards removed.

● Shuffle the cards and deal them out, face up, into 5 rows of 8 cards.

● The dealer chooses 2 cards that are next to each other and calls out their product. Do not point them out. (The product of 2 numbers is the total when they are multiplied together.)

● The other players must try to find a pair of adjacent cards with that product - the first to point them out, takes the 2 cards. (There may be 2 or 3 possible pairs. It doesn't matter if the indicated pair were not the actual ones the dealer spotted so long as their product is the same.)

● The next player then 'spots' a new pair and calls out their product.

● Take it in turns until all the cards have been won, or the remainder are so spread out that it is difficult to use them.

● The player whose cards add up to the most points is the winner.

impact MATHS HOMEWORK

Sum magic

YOU WILL NEED: a pencil and a calculator.

● Ask your partner to choose a section of the 100 square, 5 columns wide by 5 rows deep. (See the example below.)

● You can tell them very quickly that the sum of all the numbers in this 5 x 5 square section is 850.

How do you do this?!

● If you look at the middle number of the chosen section and multiply it by 25 you will have the total. (You may need to use a calculator.)

● Can you find a quick way to multiply a number by 25 in your head?

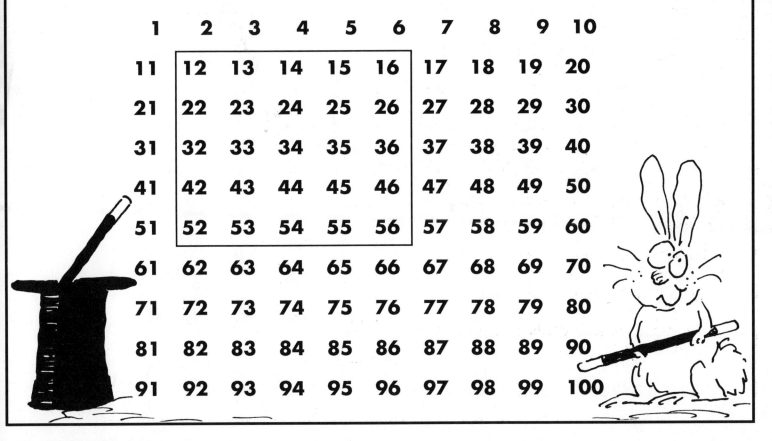

1	2	3	4	5	6	7	8	9	10
11	12	13	14	15	16	17	18	19	20
21	22	23	24	25	26	27	28	29	30
31	32	33	34	35	36	37	38	39	40
41	42	43	44	45	46	47	48	49	50
51	52	53	54	55	56	57	58	59	60
61	62	63	64	65	66	67	68	69	70
71	72	73	74	75	76	77	78	79	80
81	82	83	84	85	86	87	88	89	90
91	92	93	94	95	96	97	98	99	100

_____and

child

_____

helper(s)

_____

did this activity together

Making multiples

YOU WILL NEED: a pack of cards with the face cards removed.

● Deal out the cards one by one in a row, face up.

● After each one is dealt, study the cards in front of you. You are looking for ways of making any multiple of 7. For example:

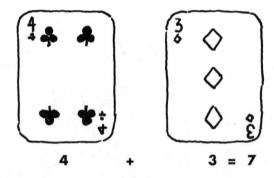

4　　　　+　　　　3　=　7

Discard the 4 and the 3 and start again.

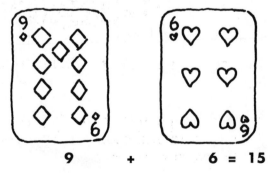

9　　　　+　　　　6　=　15

15 is not a multiple of 7 so deal another card.

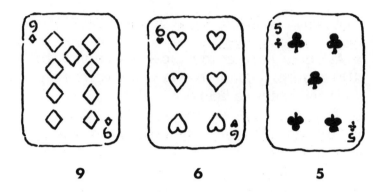

9　　　　　　6　　　　　　5

You can make a multiple of 7

9 x 6 = 54 and 54 - 5 = 49
49 = 7 x 7

● Discard these cards and carry on.

● To win you must use all the cards.

impact MATHS HOMEWORK

Score 27

YOU WILL NEED: a pack of cards with the face cards removed.

● Deal yourself 5 cards.

● You have to make 27 using all of the 5 cards in your hand using each one only once.

● You may add, subtract, divide, multiply or any combination of these rules. For example:

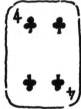

3

4

1

7   10

3 x 10   = 30
30 - 7   = 23
23 + 4   = 27
27 x 1   = 27

● When you succeed shout:

Twenty Seven!

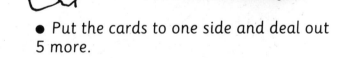

● Put the cards to one side and deal out 5 more.

● If you simply cannot make 27, deal out 1 new card and choose 1 from your hand to return to the pack.

● Play until all the cards are gone!

Dear Parent or Carer

This is a game which is much better when played co-operatively rather than competitively. As you take turns, help each other to try to find ways of making 27. How far can you get? It is not as easy as it sounds and you will need to do lots of arithmetic!

_____and

child

_____

helper(s)

_____

did this activity together

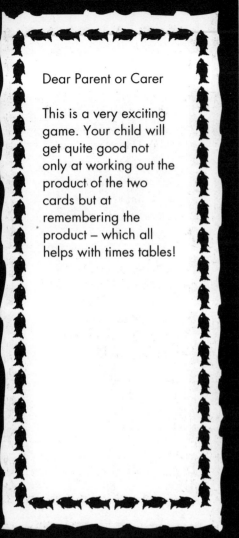

_____and

child

_____

helper(s)

_____

did this activity together

Number

Small fortune

YOU WILL NEED: a pile of small counters for each player, such as pasta spirals, Lego bricks, dried beans or raisins, and a pack of cards with the face cards removed.

● Deal one card, face down, to each player. Look at your card then, depending upon the size of the card, you may place one, or more, of your counters in the middle of the table.

● Deal a second card to each player. After looking at the card, those who wish to may gamble another one, or more, counters.

● When everyone has done this, turn your cards face up.

● Each player must now say the product of their 2 cards out loud.

● The player with the highest product wins the pile of counters from the centre of the table.

● Put the cards on the bottom of the pack and continue the game until someone runs out of counters.

Point the way

YOU WILL NEED: a pack of cards with the 10s and face cards removed and a board like the one below for each player.

● Take it in turns to pick up a card and place it, face up, on your board.

● Once you have put it down, it may not be moved.

● Once you have placed a card on your board, you must add together the values of the cards as in the example below. Now what is your total?

● Continue taking cards in turn until you each have 5 cards on your board.

● The aim is to achieve a total as near as possible to the number 9.9.

● Write your final score in the space at the top. Nearest to 9.9 wins. If your cards total more than this, you are bust!

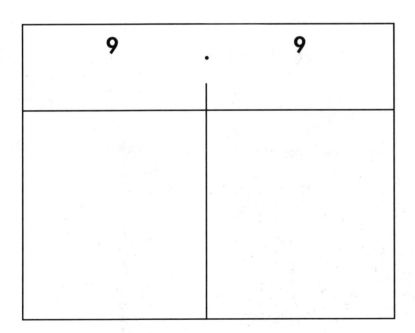

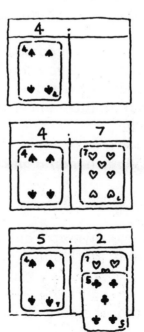

Dear Parent or Carer

This game will help your child to understand why we sometimes need to use decimal points in a number. It is important to realise that if the left-hand column goes over ten, you add one to the right-hand column and vice versa. There is quite a degree of strategy in placing cards sensibly!

_____and

child

_____

helper(s)

_____

did this activity together

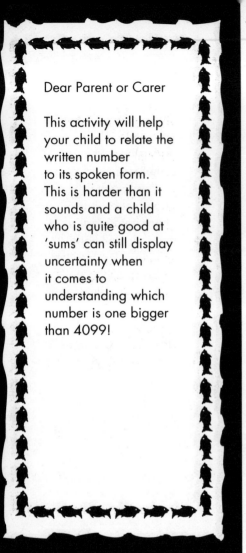

_____and

child

_____

helper(s)

_____

did this activity together

Number test

YOU WILL NEED: a pencil and paper and lots of people to talk to!

● Prepare a list of 3-figure numbers. (You need about 8 altogether!)

● Make the last one a 4-figure number which ends in 099, such as:

4099

● Ask a grown-up if they will help you with a number experiment. Tell them you won't be asking them to do hard sums!

● You are going to read your list of numbers out loud. Each time you say a number, the grown-up has to write down the number that is 1 larger than the number you say. For example:

You say **'Three hundred and forty-six'**.

They should write **347**.

● Check the grown-up's answers. (It will help to work out the answers in advance!)

It's likely that they are all correct except the last one!

Did they write **5000**?

If the grown-up got the last one right, they ought to be a maths teacher!

● Try this test on as many people as you can. How many got it right?

Wrong!

Ginormous numbers

YOU WILL NEED: a pencil and paper and a calculator.

● Think of a really big number, such as:

One million, seven hundred and sixty-two thousand, six hundred and forty-five!

Say it out loud, and at the same time enter it on the calculator. (Do not show your partner.)

● Your partner must write this down in figures:

1,762,645.

● Then you both check it!

● Now let your partner choose a number.

● Take 2 or 3 turns each.

● Arrange your ginormous numbers in order, from smallest to largest.

Dear Parent or Carer

This activity will help your child with the difficult skill of understanding and ordering very large numbers. Even children who are quite good at 'sums' can sometimes have difficulty with very large numbers.

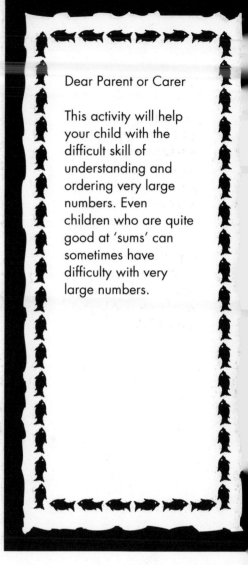

_____and

child

_____

helper(s)

_____

did this activity together

_____and

child

_____

helper(s)

_____

did this activity together

Card race

YOU WILL NEED: a pack of cards with the face cards removed.

● Place 1 card, face up, in the middle and deal 4 cards to each player. Place the rest in a pile, face down.

● Each player must use any, or all, of their cards to make the number on the card in the middle – they may add, subtract, divide or multiply.

● The first player to make the number calls out and collects the card in the middle.

● Take back the cards and deal again.

The first to collect 5 cards is the winner.

impact MATHS HOMEWORK

One million words

How fat would a book have to be to contain 1,000,000 words?

- First of all, ask people to guess. (Look at a fairly large book to give some idea how fat it would need to be... 10 cms... 50 cms... 100 cms?)

- Record the guesses of everyone you ask.

Name	10cm	50cm	100cm

- Now work it out.

> **Calculate how many words there are on 1 page. (You can do this by working out how many words there are on a line and then how many lines there are on a page).**

- Then work out how many pages you would need to have 1,000,000 words.

- How thick would that make the book?

Dear Parent or Carer

This activity encourages your child to develop the skill of making sensible mathematical judgements. Trying to calculate the actual number of pages and the size will also involve a degree of arithmetical thinking and skill.

_____and

child

_____

helper(s)

_____

did this activity together

Are you square?

YOU WILL NEED: a bag; a pencil and paper for each player and 9 cards with 1, 1, 1, 4, 4, 4, 16, 16, 16 written on them (you can make these by cutting up old birthday or Christmas cards, or an old cereal packet).

● Each player must write a list of all the even numbers from 2 to 50.

● Now put the cards inside a bag and shake them up.

● Take it in turns to take out 2, 3, 4 or 5 cards.

● Try to make any of the numbers on your list by adding up the numbers on the cards. Then cross off the number(s) on the list.

● Put the cards back after each turn.

The first player to cross 15 numbers off their list is the winner.

impact MATHS HOMEWORK

Teachers' Notes
YEAR SIX

The activities in this book also address aspects of the Programme of Study in Number. In particular, this section utilises the following skills:

- counting, reading, writing and ordering the whole numbers;
- using a thorough understanding of place value to enable problems to be solved and complex computations to be performed;
- utilising and applying a variety of computational methods, both mental and written, involving multiplication, division, addition and subtraction;
- exploring numerical relationships and patterns, including some elements of generalisation;
- consolidating all number facts;
- utilising fractions, decimals and percentages, and
- investigating numbers and numerical patterns in a variety of different contexts.

Rugby line-up Children will need to compare results and check each other's sums. It is usually best to have done the sums yourself beforehand and have them written on a large sheet of paper for the children to use as a check list. It is helpful to demonstrate how they can get the large numbers on the calculator by changing the answer from minutes to hours, to days, and so on, as they go.

Famous fives Children can work in groups and compare the methods they used. Are there several ways of making one number, for example ten? Can you collectmand display all the different ways you find? are sp,e mi,ners impossible or very difficult to make? Put nup a list of these so that the children can keep trying in their spare moments!

Puzzles Children can make a whole class book or a wall display of their puzzles. Everyone can join in, since the puzzles can involve maths at any level - some of the simpler ones can be just as hard to solve if you don't know the answer! Encourage the children to use their knowledge of number relationships, for example tens and units. 'I have a tens digit which is twice my units digit, and a hundreds digit which is twice my tens digit. What number could it be?'

Cross numbers The value of this activity - aside from its skills practice aspects - really lies in encouraging children to create their own puzzles. This is much harder than it looks, especially if you lay down criteria, such as the pattern of black and white squares must be symmetrical. Finished cross number puzzles make a fine display on black and white paper!

Great difference This activity has several possible solutions. Encourage children to talk about the strategies they used. Do they think that their solution is the best? Suppose the rules were reversed and they had to get the smallest total possible? Would their strategies be the same?

Three for luck Children can work in pairs and lay out three cards. How many different numbers can they make using only those three cards? Collect together the answers from several pairs of children and display them as number sentences (for example 3 x 4 + 6 = 18) around three central cards (a three, a four, and a six).

Dicey tables Children can discuss which numbers were hard to cross out and which ones were easy. Was seven times their table number easy? Was ten times harder? Working in pairs, can they make a chart of the number of throws it takes to get seven as an answer with two dice if you add the dice, and then the number of throws it takes to get eight and so on. Can they learn anything from their findings?

Percentage challenge This game is difficult but children often get hooked and wish to keep playing it back in class. It is a good idea if they record their games - then if someone succeeds in reducing 60 to zero, at least it is recorded! They can start with different numbers. What makes a number a good one to start with?

Making history Children can collate their results. What was the highest number they tried. Wich primes can be made as six times the number plus one and which ones can be made as six times the number minus one? Put them in two sets for the purposes of display. Which of the numbers made as above are not primes?

Prime time The children's results can be collected into a class book or class display. Which numbers did they try? Which numbers got left out? Did they try out some really big numbers? Can any of the children suggest a reason why this conjecture sounds plausible?

Be a millionaire Collect together all the children's ways of making the different coins. Did anyone think of a way that no-one else found? How many ways did the children find for making each coin? Were some coins easier to make than others?

Display all the coins with the various ways of making their value.

How old? This activity can be used to make a class book of the children's puzzles. These can involve all levels of mathematics and indeed, the simpler puzzles can sometimes be the hardest. Encourage children to use squares, cubes, primes and factors in the puzzles: 'My factors (not including myself and one) add to one more than the number I am. Which number am I?' Answer = 20.)

Tables patience Children can play this game in pairs in class, recording their moves in written form. Thinking of a way to record the cards they cover up is quite difficult,. However, if they succeed at the

game they will have a complete record of how they did so!

Sixes out Children can play this game in groups of three or four in class. What is a sensible number of times to throw the dice before passing them on? How likely are you to throw one six/two sixes? Some children may want to work out the exact probabilities by working out all the possible combinations they can throw with the dice.

Shriek! Children can do a great deal of work based on the concept of Shriek! The number of combinations or ways of arranging three things is three. The number of ways of arranging five things is five. Ask the children to check this by working it out with low numbers. Can they see why this is the case?

Favourite number line-up Children can be encouraged to try this with larger numbers. Can they see why it works? A good way of working this out is to work out what three times 37037 is!

Multiplication marathon In class, you could asks groups of children to do a real multiplication marathon to see how large a

total they can reach. They can take it in turns to do the multiplication sums, each taking over the number reached by the last player, writing down their throw and the new sum each time. Display the longest and most specticular sums on the wall.

Phone book count-up Children's estimates and their ways of working out the actual number can be shared in class. Which do they think is the best way? Can they come up with better ways to find the exact number by working together? Is there any way of checking?

Magical 6174 Which numbers did the children try out at home? Did they all work? Which numbers didn't work at all (for example 4,444)? The children will have some which turned into 6174 very quickly, and others that took a long time. Ask them to classify them into sets according to how many steps they took.

Book tax Compare the prices of books that the children are talking about and the amounts of VAT. Why are some books more expensive than others, for example hardback/paperback, and so on? Can the

children find the VAT on other items? How about television sets or Walkman's ... ?How much less would they pay without the tax?

Does it divide? This work can all be shared back in class. The children can generate three-figure numbers by throwing a dice three times or taking three cards from a pack of cards. Does their three-figure number divide by two, by three, by four or by five? They can play a game in which they score points for any factor. For example: if it divides by five, score five. How many numbers can they make using the three figures generated by the dice? How high a score can they get?

Spreadsheet challenge Children can compare spreadsheets. They can check each other's for errors and accuracy. Can they create a giant spreadsheet between a group of four of them where there is a relationship between each of the vertical numbers as well as the horizontal ones, for example: the first rule is x2+0, the second rule is x2+1 and so on?

impact MATHS HOMEWORK

Rugby line up

YOU WILL NEED: a calculator to work this out!

There are 15 players in a rugby team. The 'All-yellows' team have won the cup. They are having a big argument about the order in which they should line up to collect the prize cup!

The manager agrees to try out all the different arrangements. If he can try out a new order of players once a minute, he calculates it shouldn't take very long to try them all out.

One of his players laughs! He thinks it will take over a million years!

Who is right?

(NOTE: The number of different possible arrangements of 15 different objects is
15! = 15 x 14 x 13 x 12... and so on).

If the player is right, you may need to think hard about how to fit this on your calculator!

Dear Parent or Carer

This activity requires your child to make a sensible estimate and then check the answer! The numbers get surprisingly large, and you will both have to think very hard about how to use the calculator.

_____and

child

_____

helper(s)

_____

did this activity together

impact MATHS HOMEWORK

Famous fives

George said to Anne, 'Actually, I believe that it is possible to make any number out of five 5s!'

Anne was sceptical. 'I don't believe it', she replied.

So George decided to prove her wrong!

For example:

$$1 = \frac{5 \times 5 + 5 - 5}{5}$$

$$2 = \frac{5 + 5 + 5 - 5}{5}$$

Timmy, the dog, came up with the hardest sum.

$$\Sigma 5 + 5 - \frac{5}{5} + 5 = 24$$

($\Sigma 5$ means $1 + 2 + 3 + 4 + 5$)

● Working with someone in your house, see how many numbers you can make using only five 5s.

impact MATHS HOMEWORK

Puzzles

- Can you find the answers to these puzzles?

- Can you work out a foolproof way of solving them?

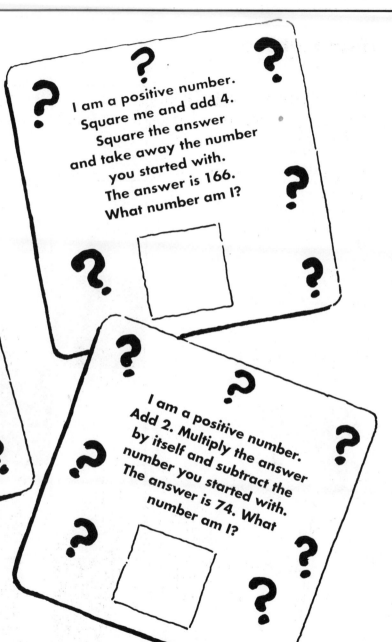

I am a positive number. Add 10. Find the square root and the answer is 7. What number am I?

I am a positive number. Square me and add 4. Square the answer and take away the number you started with. The answer is 166. What number am I?

I am a positive number. Add 2. Multiply the answer by itself and subtract the number you started with. The answer is 74. What number am I?

- Make up some more puzzles like this for friends in school.

_____and

child

_____

helper(s)

_____

did this activity together

Cross numbers

● Can you fill in the puzzle?

ACROSS
1 (2 x 46) + 1
3 4 x 7 doubled
5 198 ÷ 2
8 7 x 6
9 7 squared less 1
10 1 - 1

DOWN
1 3 squared x 11
2 3 x 13 x 10
4 6 x 11
6 8 x 9 or 6 x 12
7 144 ÷ 6

Great difference

● Ask someone to help you arrange the numbers 1 to 9 in the circles so that when you add the differences between adjacent numbers you get the largest score possible.

The box opposite is an example of how to play.

● Try several times. What's your largest score?

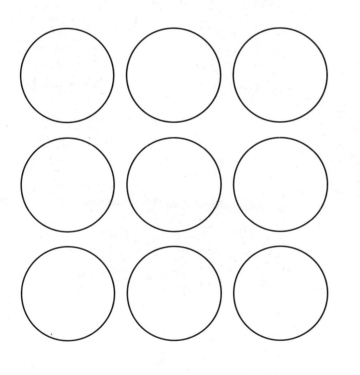

The top row could be: ⑨ ① ⑧

and the next row could be: ② ⑦ ③

which gives a score so far of: **(9 - 1)**

+ (9 - 2) + (8 - 1) + (8 - 3) + (7 - 1)

+ (7 - 2) + (7 - 3) + (9 - 7) + (8 - 7)

+ (2 - 1) + (3 - 1) = 48 Whew!

Dear Parent or Carer

This activity involves an amazing amount of arithmetical practice. It is also very difficult to actually find a strategy which works! The more you work on it together, the more fun it will be!

_____and

child

_____

helper(s)

_____

did this activity together

_____and

child

_____

helper(s)

_____

did this activity together

Three for luck

YOU WILL NEED: a pack of cards with the face cards removed and a pencil and paper for each player.

● Place the cards in a pile, face down.

● Take it in turns to take 3 cards.

● Write down the numbers. You may add or multiply these numbers in any combinations to give your score.

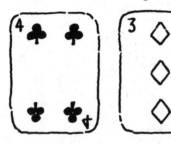

could give 9 (4 + 3 + 2 = 9)

OR 14 (4 + 3 = 7 x 2 = 14)

OR 24 (4 x 3 = 12 x 2 = 24)

and so on.

● Take 6 turns each.

● The player with a total score nearest to 99 is the winner!

impact MATHS HOMEWORK

Dicey tables

YOU WILL NEED: 2 dice.

● Each player must choose a multiplication table above 5.

● Write out all the products up to 10 times that number. For example:

6, 12, 18, 24 . . . 60

● Take it in turns to throw the 2 dice.

● Each time you throw the dice, add the scores and multiply the answer by your chosen tables number.

So if you throw a 2 and a 3
2 + 3 = 5

Your table is 6 so 5 x 6 = 30

● Cross out the 30 from your list of products.

● Continue playing. The first player to cross them all out is the winner.

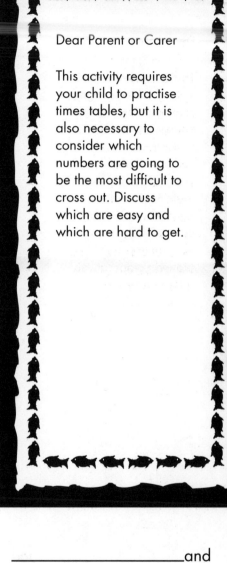

Dear Parent or Carer

This activity requires your child to practise times tables, but it is also necessary to consider which numbers are going to be the most difficult to cross out. Discuss which are easy and which are hard to get.

_____and

child

_____

helper(s)

_____

did this activity together

Percentage challenge

YOU WILL NEED: a pack of cards with the face cards removed; a pencil and paper and lots of patience!

● Deal out 5 cards, face up, in a row.

● Write 60 on a piece of paper. The aim is to reduce the 60 to 0! This is very difficult!

● Try to do this by adding or subtracting the values of the cards to make a percentage. (You do not have to use all 5 of the cards.)

● You must make a percentage which you can remove from the quantity (60) without using fractional numbers. The information on the facing page will help you.

● Every time you use some cards to make a percentage, you cover them with new cards, also face up.

This is an exciting game - we all had immense fun trying to get to 0 - but we failed! Can you and your partner do better?

Remember: 5% = ¹/₂₀, 10% = ¹/₁₀, 11% = ¹/₉, 16% = ¹/₆, 25% = ¹/₄, 33% = ¹/₃, 50% = ¹/₂

Here is an example of how to play.

5th layout

So
7 + 3 + 9 + 3 - 2 = 20
20% = ¹/₅
¹/₅ of 20 = 4
20 - 4 = 16
(your next starting total)

and so on ...

4th layout

So
1 + 9 + 6 = 16
16% = ¹/₆
¹/₆ of 24 = 4
24 - 4 = 20
(your next starting total)

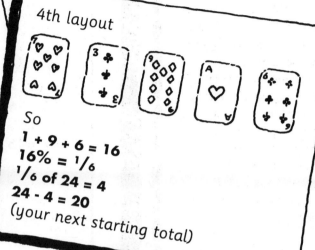

1st layout

So
3 + 7 + 8 + 10 + 5 = 33
33% = ¹/₃
¹/₃ of 60 = 20
60 - 20 = 40
(your next
starting total)

2nd layout

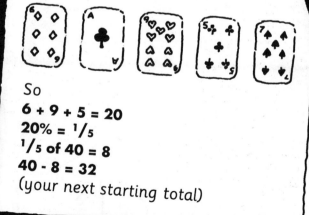

So
6 + 9 + 5 = 20
20% = ¹/₅
¹/₅ of 40 = 8
40 - 8 = 32
(your next starting total)

3rd layout

So
10 + 9 + 7 - 1 = 25
25% = ¹/₄
¹/₄ of 32 = 8
32 - 8 = 24
(your next starting total)

Making history

It is said that a prime number is usually: 6 times (something) plus or minus 1.

For example:

23 = (6 x 4) - 1

37 = (6 x 6) + 1

● Can you 'make history' and find a prime number above 10 which cannot be made like this?

Prime time

Any even number can be written as the sum of 2 prime numbers:

18 = 7 + 11

24 = 17 + 7

Test this out! Perhaps you can become world famous by finding an even number which doesn't work!

Dear Parent or Carer

This activity will involve a lot of trial and error and a great deal of arithmetical practice. It is not intended to go on for too long – just long enough to try several different numbers. Encourage your child to try large and small numbers. Can your child explain to you what a prime number is?

_____and

child

_____

helper(s)

_____

did this activity together

_____and

child

_____

helper(s)

_____

did this activity together

Be a millionaire

YOU WILL NEED: one 1p, 2p, 5p, 10p and 50p coin and a dice.

● Lay out the coins in a line.

● Throw the dice as many times as you like. You may add, subtract or multiply the numbers thrown to reach the value of any coin.

For example:

> **IF you throw**  **and** ⚀
>
> **You can say 4 - 2 = 2**
> **Then take a 2p coin.**
>
> **OR you could decide to go on throwing, saying 4 + 2 = 6**
> **Then throw the dice again.**
>
> **IF you then throw a** ⚄
>
> **You can say 5 x 6 = 30**
> **Then keep throwing the dice to try to get 50p!**

● If you get to a number larger than 50 you must pass the dice on to the next player.

● Take it in turns until all the coins are gone.

The player with the most money is the winner.

impact MATHS HOMEWORK

How old?

My mum's age is a
square number this year
and in 2 years' time will be a
cube number.
How old is she now?

● Make up another puzzle like this for a friend to try.

REMEMBER
If you multiply a number by itself you get a square number (7 x 7 = 49).

If you multiply it by itself again you have a cube number (7 x 7 x 7 = 343).

_____and

child

_____

helper(s)

_____

did this activity together

_____and

child

_____

helper(s)

_____

did this activity together

Tables patience

YOU WILL NEED: a pack of cards with the face cards removed and a lot of patience!

● Lay out 6 cards, face up, in 2 rows of 3.

● Together, you are searching for ways to make 24 or 36 using the values of the cards. You can add, subtract, divide or multiply. When you find a combination of numbers which 'works' you may cover those numbers up with new cards.

● Keep going until you cannot make 24 or 36 in any way, shape or form!

● The aim is to use all the cards in the pack.

Best of luck!

impact MATHS HOMEWORK

Sixes out

YOU WILL NEED : 2 dice and a sheet of paper to score on.

● Throw 2 dice. Multiply the values together and write down the score.

● Throw the dice again. Multiply the values and add the product to your score. (The product is the total you get when you multiply 2 numbers together.)

● You may throw the dice as many times as you like in each turn and keep adding the products to your score.

BUT if you throw a 6, you lose all your score for that turn.

AND if you throw two 6s, you lose all your score up until that point.

● You may choose to stop throwing the dice and end your turn whenever you like.

● Take it in turns to play.

The first player to reach a score of 301 is the winner!

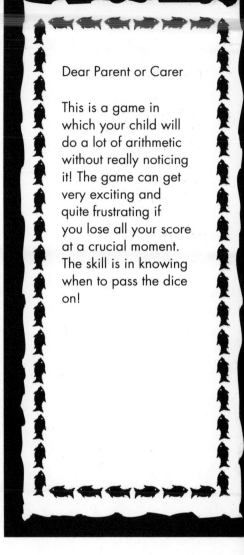

Dear Parent or Carer

This is a game in which your child will do a lot of arithmetic without really noticing it! The game can get very exciting and quite frustrating if you lose all your score at a crucial moment. The skill is in knowing when to pass the dice on!

_____and

child

_____

helper(s)

_____

did this activity together

Shriek!

In maths there is a sign which we call 'shriek'.

So **4!** is said '4-shriek'.

It means that you have to multiply that number by every number lower than it down to 1.

4! = 4 x 3 x 2 x 1 = 24

● What is **3!**?

3! =

● What is **5!**?

5! =

● Explain to someone else what **!** means and ask them to guess how much **10!** is.

● Have a guess yourself.

Do you think it is more or less than 1,000?

More or less than 10,000?

● Collect as many guesses as you can.

● Now work it out. (You may need a calculator to help you!)

Who was nearest?

Favourite number line up

● Ask someone to tell you their favourite number between 1 and 10.

● Multiply it by **37037**. (You may need a calculator!)

● Now treble your answer.

You should have a line-up of their favourite number.

● Try this with other favourite numbers.

Why does it work? Can you work it out?

Dear Parent or Carer

This activity can make a really nice 'trick' for children to try on their friends and relations. It requires quite a lot of maths - especially if they do some of the working out alone! But the really intriguing thing is why it works! Any ideas?

_____and

child

_____

helper(s)

_____

did this activity together

Multiplication marathon

YOU WILL NEED: a dice and a pencil and paper. (You may also need a calculator to check your arithmetic!)

- Throw the dice twice.

- Multiply the 2 numbers together and write down your score.

- Take it in turns to throw the dice (only once after the first turn) and multiply your score by the number thrown. For example:

If you throw a 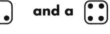 **and a**
Score = 8

On your next turn, you throw a
6 x 8 = 48
Score = 48

On your next turn, you throw a
2 x 48 = 96
Score = 96

and so on...

- Keep on playing until someone reaches a score of 999 or over!

nine hundred and ninety nine!

impact MATHS HOMEWORK

Phone book count up

How many names do you think there are in a 'phone book'?

● Ask several people to take a guess.

● Write down all their estimates in the chart below.

● Now try to discover how many names there are in the phone book and write your answer at the bottom of the chart.

name of person	guess
real number	

_____and

child

_____

helper(s)

_____

did this activity together

Magical 6174

YOU WILL NEED: a pencil and paper and a calculator.

6174 is a really amazing number. It will always appear if you follow the instructions.

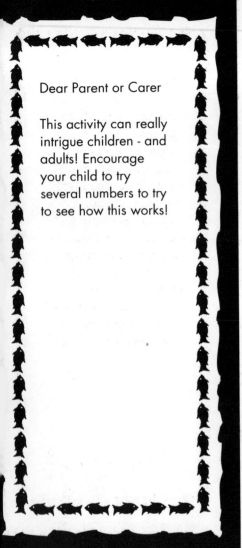

INSTRUCTIONS

● Take any 4 digits. Such as: **3590**

● Arrange them to make the largest possible number.   **9530**

● Arrange them to make the smallest possible number.   **0359**

● Find the difference between these 2 numbers (9530 – 0359).   **9171**

● Rearrange these so as to make the largest and the smallest numbers: **9711**

    1179

● Find the difference between these 2 numbers (9711 – 1179).   **8532**

● Repeat as above: **8532**
    2358-
    6174

Keep going until 6174 turns up. Amazing! Can you work out why this happens?

impact MATHS HOMEWORK

Book tax

YOU WILL NEED: a pencil and paper and a copy of your favourite book.

● Look at your favourite book.

● How much did it cost? Write down the price.

My book cost [   ]

There is a proposal to put VAT (tax) on books. If they do this, how much will your book cost then?

The information in the box may help!

> **VAT is 17½ per cent**
> **First work out 10 per cent (by dividing by 10).**
> **Then work out 5 per cent (by halving 10 per cent).**
> **Then work out 2½ per cent by halving 5 per cent.**
> **Now add all these together! That is 17½ per cent.**

● Add the 17½ per cent on to the price of your book. This will be the cost if they decide to tax books!

(If there is no price on your book then estimate its price. Most small books are around £2.50 - £3.00.)

Dear Parent or Carer

This activity will help your child to calculate useful percentages. It also provides an explanation as to why VAT always rises in steps of two-and-a-half-percent. Your child can start to work out how much VAT adds to the price of many goods and may realise that the higher the value, the greater the tax!

_____and

child

_____

helper(s)

_____

did this activity together

Does it divide?

YOU WILL NEED: a pencil and paper.

● Each player should choose a car and write down the number from its registration plate (3 digits).

● Find out which numbers are its factors. (A factor is a number which divides into it without leaving any remainder - 6 is a factor of 12.)

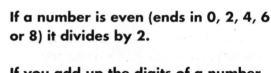

Here is some information to help you:

If a number is even (ends in 0, 2, 4, 6 or 8) it divides by 2.

If you add up the digits of a number and the total divides by 3, then the whole number divides by 3 (459: 4 + 5 + 9 = 18; 18 does divide by 3 so 459 divides by 3!).

If the number is even, halve it and, if it is still even, the number divides by 4.

If the number ends in 5 or 0, it divides by 5.

If the number is even, and its digits add up to a number that divides by 3, then the whole number divides by 6.

● Write down the factors of your car number.

● Add them up. This is your score. Who has the highest score?

● Play again. Who wins this time?

impact MATHS HOMEWORK

Spreadsheet challenge

You are going to make a number spreadsheet using the chart below.

Each row has its own rule, for example x3+2. The first row has been done for you and the second has been partly done.

● Fill in the rest of the spreadsheet yourself, inventing your own rules for each row.

1	**x3+2**	**5**	**17**	**53**
2	**x2+3**	**7**	**17**	
3				
4				
5				
6				
7				
8				
9				
10				

Dear Parent or Carer

This activity practises arithmetic skills and also reinforces children's working knowledge of spreadsheets. Please help them to think of some inventive rules.

_____and

child

_____

helper(s)

_____

did this activity together

Scottish National Guidelines Mathematics 5–14

The activities in this book cover the following strands and levels for the **Number, Money and Measurement** Attainment Targets:

Range and Type of Numbers
Levels A–E, except negative numbers
Money
Levels A–D
Addition and Subtraction
Levels A–E, except negative numbers
Multiplication and Division
Levels B–E
Round Numbers
Levels B–D
Fractions, Percentages and Ratios
Levels B–E, except ratios

Northern Ireland Programme of Study for Mathematics at Key Stage 2

Number

Understanding number and number notation

Pupils should have opportunities to:
a read, write and order whole numbers, initially to 100 and progressing to using any whole number, understanding that the position of a digit signifies its value; use their understanding of place value to develop computational methods;
b extend understanding of place value to include decimals, initially to one decimal place and then up to two places; use this to multiply and divide numbers by 10, 100 and 1000;
c estimate within calculations, initially with numbers within 100 and extending to all whole numbers to the nearest 10 or 100; approximate numbers to the nearest 10 or 100; estimate and approximate to gain a feeling for the size of a solution to a problem;
d understand and use, in context, vulgar fractions, decimal fractions and percentages; understand the equivalence of simple fractions; explore the relationships between fractions and percentages.

impact MATHS HOMEWO